WITHDRAWN

JEWISH CEREMONIAL ART

A GUIDE TO THE APPRECIATION
OF THE ART OBJECTS USED IN
SYNAGOGUE AND HOME, PRINCI-
PALLY FROM THE COLLECTIONS
OF THE JEWISH MUSEUM OF THE
JEWISH THEOLOGICAL SEMINARY
OF AMERICA.

JEWISH

CEREMONIAL ART

STEPHEN S. KAYSER, *Editor*
GUIDO SCHOENBERGER, *Associate Editor*

THE JEWISH PUBLICATION SOCIETY OF AMERICA
PHILADELPHIA   5715-1955

The Jewish Museum expresses its gratitude to the following persons and institutions, whose generous contributions made possible the preparation of the exhibition in the Metropolitan Museum of Art (January-February, 1955), and also helped meet the expenses of this publication:

Henry Kauffman Foundation
Mr. and Mrs. Harry G. Friedman
Mr. Richard Goldsmith
Mr. Milton J. Karp
Mr. Samuel Lemberg
Mr. Leon Lowenstein
Mr. Harold C. Mayer
Mr. and Mrs. Henry Rosenwald
Mrs. Miriam Schaar-Schloessinger

Gratitude is also expressed to all those individuals and institutions whose donations of objects have enriched the Museum's collection, many of whose names appear on the following pages.

FOREWORD
Louis Finkelstein

Pondering the verse, "This is my God, and I will glorify him (Ex. 15.2), Rabbi Ishmael, one of the foremost scholars of the Second Century, remarked, "Can a human being attempt to glorify his Maker? Obviously, then the verse really suggests that we use especially beautiful objects in the performance of His commandments. I will make a beautiful *lulab* (the bouquet of palm branch, myrtle, and willow branch, used together with the citron in the ritual of the Sukkoth festival); I will make a beautiful *sukkah* (the tent used for dwelling on that festival); I will make beautiful fringes for my garment (in accordance with Num. 15.38); I will make beautiful phylacteries (in accordance with Deut. 6.8)."

The effort to express love for God through creating beautiful ceremonial objects for His worship and His commandments is as ancient as Judaism itself. The very clothes of the Aaronid priests in the Temple reflected the desire to serve God through beautiful creations, and they were made "for splendor and for beauty" (Ex. 28.2). The Mishna records the names of the proselyte rulers, King Monobaz of Adiabene, and his mother, Queen Helene, who provided golden handles for all the vessels of the Temple used on the Day of Atonement, and a golden menorah placed over the door of the Sanctuary (Mishna Yoma 3.10). When Herod repented of his wanton destruction of so many scholars and desired to know what he could do to atone for his sins, a great surviving sage, Baba ben Butta, advised him that "having destroyed the (one) eye of the world, namely Jewish learning, he devote himself to the development of the (other) eye of the world —namely the Temple" (B. Baba Batra 4a). The building which he erected was so beautiful that it was said, "He who has not seen the Temple of Herod has not seen a beautiful building in all his life" (B. Baba Batra, *ibid.*).

Immense efforts were made to produce beautiful scrolls "written in good ink, with good pens, by competent scribes, and covered with fine silks" (B. Shabbat 133b). If one had purchased a beautiful vessel for a service, and came across a more beautiful one, he should, if he could afford it, indulge in the luxury of paying at least one third more for the second object.

Alas that virtually all this glory, created with such loving, painstaking care, has crumbled into dust. There are still available some beautifully written scrolls and other books, which have resisted the ravages of time—both the usage of eager disciples, and the wanton destruction of bitter enemies. Archaeology is uncovering such works as the paintings of the Dura Synagogue and the mosaics at Bet Alpha. But, for the most part, the works of art on which the ancient and medieval Hebrews spent so much energy, have been destroyed.

The heritage of Jewish art consists mainly of intangibles—great literature, touching melodies, beautiful ceremonials, and a harmony of life itself impressed in the Law.

Nevertheless, some tangible witnesses to the love for God and His Torah, felt by the pious men and women of earlier generations, do persist; and they are to be found in the ritual objects of home and synagogue. The remarkable collection brought together at the Jewish Museum of the Jewish Theological Seminary of America, through the loving dedication of modern men and women, at once testifies to the depth of love for God in the creators of these objects, and articulates that love for a later generation.

Professor Kayser, in his Introduction, guides the reader with great learning and care through the labyrinth of stylistic form reflected in these creations. He has himself contributed to the development of Jewish art, through his aesthetic arrangement of the materials at his disposal. The chaos of material, pouring into the Museum from various centuries and countries has, under his guidance and that of his devoted wife, herself an artist and designer, become a beautifully expressive and harmonious order, articulating in its own way the gratitude of this gifted couple for the love God has shown to them in bringing them out of the holocaust, in which so many of our brothers and sisters succumbed, and into America's freedom.

This handbook itself reflects the dedication and erudition of Dr. Guido Schoenberger, Research Fellow and Dr. Kayser's associate at the Jewish Museum, who has used his unchallenged experience in identifying old silver to make this cataloguing competent.

The building in which the Jewish Museum is normally housed, the former home of Mrs. Felix M. Warburg and the late Mr. Warburg, expresses in its lines and structure the concept its creators had of the home as a sanctuary. It is eminently fitting that this home, the creation of Felix M. Warburg's imagination, should be permanently associated with the fine collection which has been brought together there.

To the student of Torah it seems that the Divine inspiration, which enables gifted men to create beautiful objects, has at least for one of its purposes, the ennoblement of human character and, through that, the declaration of the glory of God. If serving God through the performance of His commandments with beautiful ceremonial objects is especially meritorious, one of the reasons may be that, in that way, the commandment becomes a more effective means for declaring the glory of God, and achieving the glory of Man. It is perhaps therefore appropriate to suggest that the Jewish Museum is not only a collection of beautiful objects, but the effect of beautiful deeds in the generosity reflected in its very wealth and diversity of possessions.

The love and dedication reflected in the making of these objects, in their preservation, in their collection, in their presentation to the community, and in their arrangement, reaches its culmination in the generous act of Dr. Francis Henry Taylor, Director of the Metropolitan Museum of Art, and of its Trustees, in providing opportunity to many, who would otherwise never see these objects, to study them in the setting of its marvelous exhibits. This celebration of the three-hundredth birthday of the American Jewish community is itself a beautiful expression of beautiful sentiments, for which we are all most grateful.

Harry G. Friedman has given invaluable advice and assistance in the preparation of this volume. Mr. Friedman has been a devoted friend and patron of The Jewish Museum for three decades and his contributions represent the bulk of The Museum's collections.

Acknowledgment is also made to Rena S. Lee, editorial assistant, and Frank J. Darmstaedter, photographer.

INTRODUCTION

A comprehensive exhibit of Jewish ceremonial art is certain to have two characteristic features: variety in comparison to other religions, and recency in the light of Jewish history. The existence of many different kinds of ceremonial objects is an expression of the emphasis which Judaism places on life in this world. This emphasis transforms virtually every human action into a means of communion with God: "In all thy ways acknowledge Him/And He will direct thy paths" (Prov. 3.6). Hence, Jewish life is filled with ceremonies from the cradle to the grave, from dawn to dusk, through all the seasons of the year. Many of these rituals call for ceremonial objects.

One might expect to find that these objects, essential to religious observance, had been treasured and handed down from generation to generation for many centuries. Yet it is a striking fact that scarcely more than a dozen Jewish ceremonial objects antedating the year 1500 are known in the world today. The reasons lie in the persecutions the Jews have experienced and in their wanderings; our own time has witnessed the mass destruction of many Jewish homes and houses of worship.

These tragic factors alone, however, do not explain fully the lack of old material. Surprising as it may seem, a number of types of Jewish ritualistic objects go back no more than three or four centuries. Torah ornaments, for example, in the forms in which they are known today (with the exception of the Torah headpieces), developed only during the last three centuries. It is a moot question how they may have looked before.

For a multitude of reasons, no intrinsically Jewish style in art has existed since the days of antiquity. Because very little has come down either from medieval times or from the Renaissance, we today know the baroque as the main stylistic force shaping Jewish ceremonial objects. But baroque comprises a variety of artistic expressions, in which the classical principles of the Renaissance have merged with a more dynamic impulse to reach beyond the boundaries of the physical world. In this tendency the baroque resembles medieval art, especially the late Gothic; but while the latter surges upward into the heavenly spheres, the baroque, because of its humanistic inheritance from the Renaissance, brings the heavens down into the terrestrial orbit in manifestations of glory and splendor. In any event, Jewish ceremonial art entered upon a new and decisive phase with the rise of the baroque. Almost all existing Jewish ceremonial objects show the impact of that style, except the spice container in the form of a medieval town.

When we speak of "Jewish art" we mean the arts as they are applied to Judaism. This application, of course, is made principally in those areas where art is essential as a means to an end.[1] Such a concept of Jewish art may be called functional, since it does not recognize any-

---

1. Stephen S. Kayser, "Defining Jewish Art", in *Mordecai M. Kaplan Jubilee Volume;* English Section, p. 456 ff.; N. Y., 1953.

9

thing Jewish in art unless it serves a purpose connected with Judaism as a way of life. The definition excludes creations by Jewish artists which are detached from Jewish objectives, but includes works which serve a Jewish purpose even though their makers were not Jewish: a situation quite common in western Europe before the Emancipation. Thus, while there is no Jewish style, there is a Jewish art, the Jews expressing themselves in the art-forms of the surrounding world.

The baroque style appears to have influenced first the structure of Torah Ark *(aron)*. The Torah Ark of the medieval synagogues was rather modest, whether it stood free or appeared as a part of the structure, as we can see in the few architectural and pictorial traces left from medieval times. The era in which the *aron* became the dominating feature of the entire synagogue began with the seventeenth century. It is interesting to note that, in Bohemia, Torah Arks were in some instances adaptations of altars removed from the monastery churches which had been secularized under Joseph II of Austria.

From the Torah Ark the influence of the baroque spread into all other expressions of Jewish ceremonial art. The Renaissance, in its sculpturesque approach, had subdued the forms of vegetation which in the picturesque baroque blossomed as never before. Flower vases on top of the columns on either side of the Torah Ark became a common feature. In the synagogues of eastern Europe the preference for floral ornaments took on deeper significance, being associated with the ancient idea of the Tree of Life, the main theme in all of eastern European Jewish ceremonial art.

A typical baroque feature in synagogue art is the use of the two rampant lions on either side of the Tablets inscribed with the Ten Commandments, which appear on Torah curtains and on top of the Ark. Although it seems old, this motif first appeared in the synagogue in the seventeenth century, and even at that time its permissibility was still a subject of violent rabbinic controversy.

The kingly lion, used so frequently in synagogue art because it was the emblem of Judah, the Tribe of David, is a typical Baroque animal in its powerful outline and expression of might. From a position at the base of the Torah Ark, functioning as a support—a feature preserved in numerous ceremonial objects—the lion rose to the upper part of the Ark or Torah curtain, where it became almost an obligatory feature during the last century.

The use of two rampant lions has its origin in the art of heraldry which goes back to the artistic expression of ancient Mesopotamia. There, the symmetrical arrangement of two erect creatures on either side of a tree had become a standard feature. When the two lions are shown flanking the Tablets of the law, they establish a striking connection with their ancient Babylonian predecessors. The Tablets stand for the Tree; the Torah is called the Tree of Life. Just as heraldic animals, usually lions, guard the family crest, so the two rampant lions on either side of the Tablets protect the Tree of Life.

Thus, an ancient motif which originated in the Near East, has acquired a new meaning in Jewish baroque art. It is interesting to note that the first lion, carved of stone and placed upon a Torah Ark, was the family blazon of its donor in Candia, Crete. This occurred in the 16th century and was partially responsible for the controversy over the use of lions in the synagogue. To see in this incident, however, the actual cause for introducing the lion motif to synagogue art, would be to overlook the aesthetic possibilities offered by a stylistic change.

All the other motifs used in baroque Torah ornaments, except that of the two sacred columns, can be traced back to medieval illuminated and illustrated Jewish manuscripts. While the columns appear in medieval times in a rather abstract rendition, in the baroque period they assume a more representational form.

The two twisted columns were shaped after the ancient *colonna santa* preserved in St. Peter's of Rome. To the Jews this column represented one of the two sacred, free-standing pillars, Yakhin and Boaz, in Solomon's Temple. Not before the baroque age, which was akin, stylistically speaking, to late antiquity (the actual time of origin of the legendary pillar in Rome), could the picturesque shape of the twisted column take the place of the fluted Renaissance column. Thus, the twisted columns with their assumed sacred tradition became practically the symbol for the Sanctuary of old and found their way from the Arks into Torah curtains, mantles, breastplates, and numerous other ritual objects as well as onto the title pages of books, which in turn became the main source for the designs for Torah arks, particularly in eastern Europe.

The few examples left from pre-baroque times show that the most usual ornamental motif for the Torah curtain was a brief inscription. Otherwise the fabric used, preferably brocade which revealed its Indian origin in the gold and silver pattern, was left empty of any representation. With the baroque and the greater emphasis on the picturesque, this simple curtain was ornamented with designs which at times covered a considerable part of the surface. The furnishings of the Tabernacle and Temple—the laver of the Levites, the table of showbread, the mitre of the High Priest, the altar of incense offering and, above all, the seven-branched candlestick, all motifs described in the Book of Exodus—appear often on the Torah curtain. If compared with those in earlier manuscripts, they show a tendency towards greater realism. The same can be said about the mantles for the Torah which, so far as ornamentation is concerned, are only variations of Torah curtains.

The Sephardim, the Jews whose ancestry dates back to pre-Inquisition Spain, never used the breastplate; nor is it used in the Sephardic synagogue today. The breastplate for the Torah is an Ashkenazic creation. (Ashkenazim are those Jews whose history is mainly connected with central and eastern Europe.) Research has failed to trace the breastplate in Germany farther back than the sixteenth century. The oldest Torah breastplates preserved date back to the seventeenth century, the great age of the Baroque, the earliest known having been dedicated in 1612 in Amsterdam. It contains an exchangeable plaque in the center, which indicated the Sabbaths on which that particular

Torah Scroll was to be used. This innovation seems to have been the reason for the creation of the breastplate. It is easy to understand that symbolically the Torah breastplate has been related to the breastplate of the biblical High Priest.

The development of the breastplate for the Torah from the beginning of the seventeenth century involved the use of an increasing number of motifs, which are also found on Torah Arks and curtains. Even human figures, mainly those of Moses and Aaron, were introduced. The technique of embossing silver, by which new and startling effects were achieved in the Baroque period, facilitated the rendering of those pictorial details in high relief.

In silver work, the boundaries between late Renaissance and baroque are rather indistinct. This is not true of the borderline between the baroque and its modification which, under the name of rococo, marks the last phase of the baroque. The silversmiths reacted with great sensitivity to the introduction of the *rocaille* design, which loosens the ornamental symmetry and permits freer play with the refined hazards of balance. Immediately after the rise of the rococo the breastplates for the Torah showed the new asymmetrical design, but retained in their general appearance the inner strength of the baroque. Likewise, the Torah curtains, even when they employed the delicate textiles of the feminine rococo, did not deviate basically from the solemnity of the masculine baroque in design.

When the rococo was superseded by classicism, the Ark and the breastplate reflected the change from motion to repose. The twisted columns frequently gave way to prismatic pillars with straight fluting. The flower motifs of the baroque were retained, however, and they blossomed out again profusely in a manner which became known as the second baroque, one of the revivals during the Victorian period. The huge breastplates designed in Austria and especially in Hungary during the second half of the last century fall into this category.

We cannot go into a detailed discussion of such individual objects as Torah crowns, cases for the Scroll of Esther, *ethrog* boxes, spice containers, and even skull caps for the High Holidays, all of which show the influence of the baroque style. Suffice it to point out that the pewter Hanukkah lamps of the eighteenth century, one of the most original Jewish creations, show in their outline the decorative baroque curves which give their design its basic character.

The reason for this strong impact of the baroque on Jewish ceremonial art lies, above all, in the historic situation. Although the baroque age was one of great disaster for many Jewish communities, especially in eastern Europe, it encompasses also the extension of the central European Jewish settlement, the resultant broadening of Jewish enterprises, and the rise of new types, such as the "Court Jew" and the princely merchant with international connections. Jewish life changed. The outside world knocked at the door of the Jew and when it entered the Jewish home it did so in a less hostile way than in preceding centuries. The scope of Jewish life broadened and so did the synagogue, particularly because many building restrictions imposed upon the Jew by the hostile non-Jewish community were lightened.

In addition, the baroque allowed a greater use of ornamental motifs and the employment of gold. The biblical description of the ancient Sanctuary speaks of an abundance of gold used for the Temple in Jerusalem and, for that matter, for the Tabernacle in the wilderness as well. This was not an extravagance, since gold in ancient times apparently was not the most precious metal, a deduction which we make from the fact that the Bible invariably mentions silver first when it speaks of silver and gold. The brilliant colors of the baroque, particularly its preference for red velvets with gold embroidery, influenced the fashioning of Torah curtains and kept the synagogues colorful and rich in ornamentation.

The 29th Psalm can well serve as a motto for Jewish baroque art when it says: "Ascribe unto the Lord, oh ye sons of might, ascribe unto the Lord glory and strength. Ascribe unto the Lord the glory due unto His name; *worship the Lord in the beauty of holiness.*" Synagogue art, especially of the seventeenth and eighteenth centuries, has to be understood in this light. It can then be left to those who approach religious art without bias to judge whether these objects are "only of the most secondary interest or value"[2] as far as their artistic appearance is concerned, or whether they deserve a real place in the development of art. To restore these ceremonial objects to their true position does not mean that we should remain smugly uncritical of their stylistic peculiarities. But our judgment of these objects must then extend into wider criticism of the forms of expression in the baroque age in general.

The Jewish ceremonial objects of the seventeenth and eighteenth centuries cannot be pushed into the background as if they were of only remote parochial relevance, since to do this would be to ignore the fact that many of them were shaped by the foremost Christian silversmiths of their time. Guild restrictions which prevailed until the Emancipation excluded Jewish craftsmen from the activities of goldsmiths. Thus non-Jewish masters like M. Wolf of Augsburg (end of the seventeenth century) or Jeremiah Zobel of Frankfort-on-the-Main (beginning of the eighteenth century) became important interpreters of Jewish ceremonial art. As already indicated, we must accept the fact that Jewish art does not necessarily have to be produced by Jewish artists and artisans. The Christian masters carefully followed the advice and wishes of those who commissioned the objects for Jewish ritual use.

While Jewish art claims the right to be judged in the light of general aesthetic considerations, one must always bear in mind its basic character: that it has been created for a specific religion. To understand Jewish art it is necessary first to understand the formative forces of Judaism. Above all, one must realize that the Bible, and particularly the Five Books of Moses, the Torah, is not the only constituent of historical Judaism. To this written tradition was added the oral tra-

2. Heinz Politzer, "The Opportunity of The Jewish Museum", in *Commentary;* vol. 7, No. 6; June, 1949, p. 590.

dition, the Talmud. Torah and Talmud together form the basis of the Jewish faith. The realm of the Bible widens into the large field of rabbinic interpretations and codifications of post-biblical times. Practically all the customs and ceremonies which find expression in Jewish ceremonial art have to be understood in the light of the development of Judaism, especially in talmudic times, that is to say, in late antiquity. Biblical precepts, history, interpretations, various customs and symbolic meanings, are thus merged inseparably into the basis on which individual objects and their uses developed. This may be illustrated by an example:

The foremost duty of the Jewish woman is the kindling of the Sabbath lights, a ceremony which inaugurates the holy seventh day of the week. Although the blessing which precedes the lighting of the candles speaks of light in the singular only, traditionally at least two candles are lit. This has been interpreted as a symbolic recognition of the two different wordings of the fourth commandment: *"Remember* the Sabbath day"* (Ex. 20.8); and *"Observe* the Sabbath day"* (Deut. 5.12).

This interpretation adds meaning to a simple development which had its historic roots in the physical layout of the Jewish home of ancient times. It consisted mainly of two rooms, one which would be equal to the modern drawing room and the other to the dining room. In order to bring light into the home on Sabbath eve, which in a literal application of the Sabbath laws would be completely dark, the Pharisees insisted on the custom of kindling lights before the Sabbath commenced; and thus it became customary to kindle one light in *each* room. This accounts for the plurality of the Sabbath lights which in later times gave rise to the interpretation just mentioned. From this also developed a charming feature in the Sabbath Lamp, used in central, western and southern Europe, which usually employed an even number of lights. Based on the forms of Roman oil lamps, the Sabbath Lamps were always formed in the shape of a star.

The Sabbath lights are characteristic for a religion in which light and the act of lighting play a dominant role. This can be illustrated by its oldest visible mark of identification—the seven-branched candlestick. According to the biblical narrative, its shape in all details is based upon divine inspiration; and no changes, essentially, have been made to the present time. Thus, although it is fashioned by man, its form is not the result of a gradually developing process.

The seven-branched candlestick, or Menorah, seems to have been particularly important during the Second Jewish Commonwealth in the Temple of Jerusalem. Unquestionably, it became the most important Jewish pictorial motif after the ancient sanctuary had ceased to exist. From an implement it had changed into an emblem. Erwin R. Goodenough, in a chapter about the Menorah in the late antique world,[3] has tried to show that it had an ornamental use, as well as

3. Erwin R. Goodenough, "Jewish Symbols in the Greco-Roman World", New York, 1954; chapter 4 (The Menorah), pp. 71-99.

a functional one. He seems to be confusing representation with actual use, a theory unsupported by any archaeological evidence. Contrary to Goodenough's assumption, the *representation* of the seven-branched candlestick was never forbidden by the rabbis. They forbade only the making of objects which were an exact replica of those once in actual use in the services of the Temple in Jerusalem. There is no evidence whatever that a seven-branched candlestick was ever used in a synagogue before the time of the Emancipation and no piece is preserved which would testify to its use in the Jewish home of that era.

The Menorah can thus be called a *symbol* of Judaism, perhaps its only symbol in the strict sense of the word, and even in this respect we had rather speak of it as a *motif*, because Judaism does not use symbols of a visual kind for the interpretation or practice of its basic beliefs. The representation of the Menorah on other ritual objects is best understood as a reminder of the period when the Temple in Jerusalem, of which the Menorah was an important part, still existed. At the same time, the fact that its actual use in the synagogue was forbidden shows that the rabbis did not want the synagogue to become a surrogate for the Temple of old. An appreciation of this fact is important for the understanding of Judaism and especially of Jewish ritual art.

In the Temple of old the priests officiated and the Levites assisted them. Without the priest the Temple is unthinkable. The synagogue, on the other hand, does not have a priest, and the rabbi is not to be compared with the priestly officials of the ancient Temple. Any layman, if sufficiently learned, can take over the functions of the rabbi; but no layman could replace the priest. While the daytime services in the synagogue parallel the order of the Temple services, the main feature of the Temple service, namely, the bringing of sacrifices, is lacking in the synagogue, which has no altar of any kind. The Torah Ark is not an altar, but merely helps to establish a meaningful spiritual relationship between the synagogue and the Temple.

Not only the synagogue, also the Jewish home is linked with the biblical Temple. The rabbis urged every Jew to approach his table with the same reverence with which the High Priest of old approached the Temple altar. The washing of the hands before partaking of food, far from originating in hygienic considerations, relates symbolically to the act of purification which was required of everyone who entered the Sanctuary in Jerusalem. Aware of this relationship, the Jew made his home a *mikdash me'at*, a little sanctuary.

The Sabbath lamp became its hallmark. Cups, spice boxes, plates for several occasions, and numerous other utensils, reflected impressively the principal Jewish idea of life—namely, its sanctity. The various objects necessary for these ceremonies are used for lighting, washing, drinking, eating, smelling. In other words, their functioning encompasses all the senses, including hearing, since the intonation of the blessings is a necessary accompaniment to the ceremonies. But everything shaped by the arts has a life of its own, determined by its form and enhanced by its ornamentation. While the latter should be part of a form in itself, it represents the merging of many elements which must be defined.

The role of the furnishings of the ancient Sanctuary as ornamentation has already been discussed. While they are depicted in a representational way, they do not conflict with the biblical prohibition which finds its main expression in the wording of the second Commandment: "Thou shalt not make unto thee a graven image nor any manner of likeness of anything that is in heaven above, or that is in the earth beneath, or that is in the water under the earth" (Ex. 20.13). This text makes it clear that the prohibition directed against idol worship is based upon the concept of a Deity whose greatness exceeds the reach of human imagination.

While the Commandment seems to preclude clearly the use of any human and animal form, it is a fact that figural representations, not only of animals but of human beings as well, appear rather frequently on Jewish ceremonial objects. Medieval manuscripts show an abundance of human figural representations. Boaz Cohen has pointed out that "Scripture never banned painting on a flat surface or, for that matter, plastic figures, if they were designed merely for an ornamental or useful end." He states furthermore: "Despite occasional deviations and the normal temptation to emulate the fine arts of their day, pious and traditional-minded Jews of every age, in consonance with the letter and spirit of the Jewish law, eschewed sculpture in relief and in the round of the completely articulated human figure."[4] How then are we to understand the appearance of figures of Moses and Aaron in relief on Torah Breastplates and that of full round figurines on spice boxes, candleholders, Hanukkah menoroth, and other objects?

A closer inspection of those figures shows that in most cases their faces have been mutilated, usually by having the nose chipped off. This makes them incomplete and therefore permissible, according to rabbinic ruling.

These figures on ceremonial objects go back no further than the seventeenth century so far as extant items are concerned. The questions regarding the use of figural representations in sculptured form evidently came up as early as the twelfth century, when French Jewish scholars permitted statuary of the *incomplete* human figure. It seems impossible, however, that figures of this nature were used on ceremonial objects during the Middle Ages, and it is safe to assume that items showing figures in the round do not antedate the year 1600. The majority of these figures refer to the ceremony pertinent to the object on which they appear. Biblical figures like Abraham and Isaac, Moses and Aaron, Miriam, King David, and the prophet Elijah, also appear. The little statuette of Judith who was connected in legend with the Maccabees became rather popular on top of Italian and German Hanukkah lamps. The representation of that figure was frequently indistinct and therefore she was once mistaken for an emulation of the *Perseus* by Benvenuto Cellini, and, again, as Judah Maccabee, the head of Holofernes

---

4. Boaz Cohen, "Art in Jewish Law", in *Judaism, A Quarterly Journal of Jewish Life and Thought,* vol. 3, #2; Spring 1954; pp. 165-176.

which she holds being accepted as that of Judah's enemy, Lysias—a rather forced interpretation.

These figures on Jewish ceremonial objects, to be sure, play only a subordinate role. They underline the meaning of the object on which they are placed, but they are by no means indispensable. As a matter of fact, they disappeared at the beginning of the nineteenth century. Their existence lasted exactly as long as the baroque influence shaped Jewish ceremonial objects. (In the "second" baroque of the last century the figures of Moses and Aaron in high relief reappeared briefly on Torah breastplates.) While the presence of these figures was once felt desirable, they would be entirely out of place today. They are typical for a certain era and for certain regions, those of central and southern Europe. When they are found on eastern Europe objects, especially on Polish filigree spice towers, their origin can be traced back to the western part of Europe. There existed evidently some workshops of Polish silversmiths which imported these figurines (or rather their molds) from western craftsmen, as evidenced by their costumes.

This points up the vital factor of regional differences in Jewish art; it justifies speaking in terms of the geography as well as the history of Jewish ceremonial objects. In the Near East, the Jew had been a metal worker for two thousand years. Aside from many other things, he also made items specifically for Jewish use; yet these do not differ in form from any other objects shaped for similar purposes, such as a cup or a lamp, except for the inscriptions which abound on near-eastern Jewish objects. (The Torah cases made of silver and sometimes of wood are, of course, in a class by themselves.)

In western countries any undamaged silver cup could be called a *kiddush* cup, especially when it was inscribed. Aside from this practice, there arose in western Jewry a growing desire to create certain types of item which developed a form of their own, although the prevailing style of the surrounding world had of necessity to be used in order to bring that form to life. The results were genuine Jewish creations such as Hanukkah lamps, containers for the *ethrog* (a fruit used on Sukkoth), the *seder* plate with three tiers, and so on. Within the framework of these categories various countries have developed types of their own: A special kind of brass Hanukkah lamp is indicative of Holland; another, of Poland. The Sabbath lamp of the central European region differs from the lamp made for the same purpose in Italy or Holland. The difference becomes particularly obvious in the ornamentation, which has a greater tendency towards the representational and the clearly outlined detail in western countries, as against the more abstract trend which pervades all of eastern European art in the Jewish realm. It is here that a typical folk art developed, favored by the more abstract tendencies which underlie the Jewish ceremonial art of this region; whereas the west, with its more distinct tastes in ornamentation, had to lean much more on trained craftsmanship. This does not mean that folk art of eastern European Jewry was lacking in artistic skill; on the contrary, certain types of work, like the paper and parchment cutouts of Poland, are outstanding examples of a highly developed artistry in handling a difficult material. These creations belong to the finest achievements of folk art in general.

In this respect mention must be made of one of the greatest contributions to the arts originating in the European east. Unfortunately, it is completely lost to us because of partial destruction and for reasons of inaccessibility. It is the art of the tombstone in Poland, Russia, and particularly in certain parts of Romania. Jewish cemeteries in these countries consist of an enormous number of sculptures in relief in which the ornamentation blends beautifully with the Hebrew inscription.

The Hebrew letter in itself is not an ornament; however, in the course of time it assumed various shapes and thereby became the most important Jewish form of ornamentation. There is no classic Hebrew letter in the sense that one has a classic Roman letter. Instead, a certain type, mainly developed in the printing plants of the last century, has usurped the place of a standard Hebrew letter, very much to its artistic disadvantage. The ceremonial objects preceding the last century, on which Hebrew letters can be found, offer striking evidence of the care with which the Hebrew letter as an ornament was used and how it was adjusted to various media, be it on embroideries or on metal. Even there one can notice the distinction between an engraving on pewter or one on silver.

The Hebrew letter at present is undergoing a renaissance in the artistic efforts of Israeli craftsmen who are reinstating it in its rightful role as the basic and most precious element in the ornamentation of Jewish objects. At the same time an attempt is being made to reshape the Jewish ceremonial objects in the artistic terms of our own time.

Many details which distinguish the objects of the past have been thrown overboard in this process. This does not make the old items obsolete. On the contrary, their message, shaped by certain stylistic necessities, is as vivid today as at the time when they originated. They should not be copied, however, as is unfortunately still being done because of the lack of good modern ceremonial designs. It will take years until the output, particularly of Israeli artists, is directed into the right channels and all the need for ritualistic objects in the modern synagogue and home can be met. When that time comes, the genuine old objects will have an especially high value because they will have gained proper historic proportion. More and more they will become a link to the past, testimonial to a living tradition which may change the outer appearance of its implements but retains always an awareness of their basic, eternal values.

JEWISH CEREMONIAL ART

1

Plate I   20

TORAH SCROLL AND ARK

The service in the synagogue consists of prayer and instruction. The latter is based upon reading and interpretation of the Bible. Among the biblical books, the Pentateuch (Five Books of Moses; *Torah*) is of particular importance. The weekly reading from it highlights the service. The important role of the Torah is emphasized by its appearance. In form it is a parchment scroll wound around wooden rods, preserving the ancient format of the book. In late antiquity precious writings were kept on two rods, which evidently led to the two rollers for the Torah Scroll.

The material originally used for synagogue scrolls was leather made of the skins of clean animals. Parchment later became the standard material for the scrolls in western countries. To this very day the Near East prefers leather for the Torah Scroll.

In antiquity the Torah Scrolls were rather small in size in comparison to the large scrolls which have been in common use in European countries since the Middle Ages. European scrolls, in turn, have influenced the size of the scroll used now in the Near East and North Africa. There the Torah is placed in an outer case of metal or wood which opens and in which the Torah remains even when it is read. More usual today is the practice of draping fabric covers (or mantles) over the Torah Scroll when it is closed after the reading.

The Hebrew text of the Torah is written by hand, without punctuation or vowel points. Elaborate rules and regulations govern the writing, and because of strong and unbroken tradition the Torah Scrolls have not changed in appearance for many centuries.

The Torah Scroll is the most sacred of all objects in the synagogue. The table on which it is placed while being read to the congregation has to be covered with a cloth. As a mark of respect the congregation rises when the holy Scroll is lifted up after it is read. It is an honor to be called to the Torah during the reading. Worshippers who pass the Scroll kiss its mantle.

The Torah Scrolls are placed within the Ark, the most important architectural feature of the synagogue. It is called *Holy* Ark after the Ark of the Covenant in the Tabernacle and in the Temple of biblical times. The worshippers, when praying, face the Holy Ark. Before its doors (in Mediterranean countries inside of them) hangs a curtain called the *Parokheth* which in many cases has a shorter valance called the *Kapporeth*, also referring to the description of the furnishings of the Tabernacle in the Book of Exodus.

The history of the Ark shows a development from an original movable receptacle which was brought into the hall of worship and taken out again when the service was over, to a permanent architectural part of the synagogue building. This development accounts for the freestanding Torah Ark which can be found mainly in the synagogues of northern countries. The commonly accepted type of Torah Ark, which was recessed in the wall, gave rise to the Torah curtains. They became particularly rich in plastic embroideries in central Europe.

°[1.] TORAH ARK   S 1431

Wood, carved and painted.
H. 94"   L. 110"   D. 34"
Urbino, Italy, Inscription date 1451

Rectangular shape in two horizontal divisions. Upper portion, having a break front, is divided into four cupboards, with hinged doors, by seven pilasters of the composite order, the shafts fluted and astragalled, the capitals carved and the bases molded. Cupboard doors are divided by molded stiles into three panels, each large central panel decorated with a painted arabesque pattern upon a gilt ground. Inner sides of the doors are fitted with sliding panels decorated with Hebrew inscriptions in gold on red grounds. Lower portion is similarly divided into four cupboards by paneled pilasters upon paneled pedestals. The hinged doors have single molded panels, decorated with painted arabesques on blue grounds, the moldings of the pedestal gilded. On a molded base. Sides paneled and decorated, similar to front.

Inscriptions mainly passages from the Psalms and other biblical quotations, including the Ten Commandments. Also an inscription that this Ark was a gift to the synagogue of Urbino, Italy, in the year 1451.

Benguiat Collection

PLATE I

[2.] TORAH ARK (RECONSTRUCTION)   S 727

Wood.
H. 119"   W. 76½"   D. 20½"
Cairo, Egypt, 13th century
Reconstruction of socle and shrine, 1902

One of the most interesting pieces of ecclesiastical furniture in this country. This interest is focussed in the fact that most of the frontal boards and inscriptions are original and come from the Orient, where they probably served the same purpose for many centuries. The Hebrew inscriptions upon the boards also point to their great age, as evidenced by the ancient abbreviation of the name of the Almighty. The top inscription only is a modern restoration.

The inscribed boards were found in Cairo in a Genizah ("place of storing away"), where many other important documents of Jewish antiquity were brought to light.

Inscription above the doors (Ps. 24.5): "And righteousness from the God of his salvation. This is the generation of them that seek Him." On left side (Ps. 5.8): "But as for me, I will come into Thy house in the multitude of Thy mercy." On right side (Ps. 100.4): "Enter into the gates with thanksgiving and into His courts with praise: be thankful unto Him, and bless His name." These words are followed by the name apparently of the donor, "Solomon bar Yefet," who lived in Cairo in the first half of the 13th century.

On the base part, two boards, perhaps once carved for portals of synagogues. Inscriptions from Deut. 6.4 and Ps. 5.8, followed by a blessing for "Obadyah bar Yefet Abu Almuali" who defrayed

22

all the expenses of the building. Inscription on the lower board contains praise of two men. (The first part of the upper row is now in the British Museum.) The second name is "Solomon Halevi ben Tobia."

The original boards were brought from Cairo by Professor Solomon Schechter in 1902 and, upon reconstruction, the Ark was used in the synagogue of The Jewish Theological Seminary of America, New York City, from 1902 to 1932.

* 3. TORAH CASE WITH HEADPIECES   L 12-54
Case and headpieces of silver, embossed and hammered.
Torah Case: H. 23½″ D. 8″
Headpieces: H. 12″ D. 4″
From Nablus (Shechem), 18th century

Octagonal case, consisting of two equal parts held together with a hinge at back. Main pattern of the decoration, covering the entire surface, is arabesque scroll work in architectural arrangement, with five and three scalloped arches. Upper part consists of a bulbous-shaped dome and large finial with bells attached to chain. On arches, semi-precious stones.

Headpieces with three tiers and hammered abstract ornamentation; typical for Near-Eastern Torah decoration.

Lent by the Museum of the Hebrew Union College, Cincinnati, O.
                                     PLATE II

* 4. TORAH CASE   S 21
Cylindrical, inlaid copper silver arabesque ornaments.
H. 32″ D. 7″
Samaritan, Damascus, 1565
Master: Joseph

Inscriptions in Samaritan: Bible quotations praising the Lord. In addition: "In the name of God. This case for the Holy Scriptures was made in Damascus by . . . Joseph, son of Abaspoh of the tribe of Patar. Under the direction of Rabban Abi Azzai, son of Rabban Joseph in Damascus . . . of the Kingdom of the Ishmaelites." (Mohammedan era)
                                     PLATE II

* 5. TORAH ARK CURTAIN   F 3432
Needlework on canvas, embroidered with silk.
L. 70″ W. 48″
Italy, 1699
Made by Leah Otolenghi (Signed "Leah, wife of Oto," evidently an abbreviation of Otolenghi)

Center: Motifs referring to the High Holidays: New Year and Day of Atonement (Rosh Hashanah and Yom Kippur); Feast of Weeks (Shabuoth), commemorating the giving of the Ten Commandments; The Feast of Booths (Sukkoth), indicated by palm branch and citron; and finally the Rejoicing over the Law (Simhath Torah), with table for wine and food. The unique character of this curtain is in the side decorations, a series of cartouches referring to special Sabbaths and the appropriate sections read from Scripture.

Right Side: (1) Half shekel (coin) referring to the payment of the half shekel by every male adult (Ex. 30.13). (2) Tombs of

3

4

Plate II   24

the patriarchs and matriarchs, referring to the death and burial
of Sarah (Gen. 23). (3) Table for the Passover meal and the
Paschal Lamb, referring to the Sabbath preceding Passover (Ex.
12.5). (4) Hanukkah Menorah, referring to the Sabbath during
Hanukkah (Num. 8.2). (5) The New Moon, referring to the beginning of the month of Nisan in which Passover falls (Ex. 12.2).
Left Side: (1) Throne and hand, referring to the Sabbath preceding Purim (Ex. 17.16): ("The hand is on the throne of the
Lord that there will be war with Amalek from generation to
generation." (Amalek typifies Israel's enemies.)) (2) Mount of
Olives, referring to the verses from the Book of Zachariah, read
on the Sabbath during the Feast of Booths (Zach. 14.4): ("And
His feet shall stand in that day upon the Mount of Olives.") (3)
Walled city of Jerusalem and the Temple, referring to the Sab-
bath following the Ninth of Ab, the day of the destruction of the
Temple (Isaiah 40.1): ("Comfort ye, comfort ye, My people.")
(4) Scroll of Esther on desk, referring to the festival of Purim
(Esther 9.26). (5) Hands holding hyssop, referring to the Sabbath on which is read Numbers ch. 19, about ritual purification
(Inscription quotes verse 6).
Similar pieces in the Victoria and Albert Museum, Kensington, England, and in the Synagogue of Florence, Italy. (See Sol Cohen, "A
17th Century Parochet," *The Jewish Chronicle,* London, July 10, 1954,
p. 15.)
Harry G. Friedman Collection

PLATE III

* 6. TORAH ARK CURTAIN   F 2944
Gold and silver appliqué and embroidery on violet silk.
H. 85"   W. 55"
Italy, 1681

Center, Mount Sinai under heavy clouds out of which hands
emerge holding the Tablets of the Law. Below, the walled city
of Jerusalem with the Temple and its Holy of Holies.
Inscriptions: "The Lord spoke with you face to face in the mount
out of the midst of the fire" (Deut. 5.4). "Lo, I come unto thee
in a thick cloud" (Ex. 19.9). "The mountain which God has desired for His abode" (Ps. 68.17). "I set Jerusalem above my
chiefest joy" (Ps. 137.6).
"Made by Simhah, wife of Menahem Levi Meshulami." Date
1681 (indicated by dotted letters in the quotation), "He shall
receive a blessing from the Lord" (Ps. 24.5).
Harry G. Friedman Collection

PLATE IV

* 7. TORAH ARK CURTAIN   F 3580
Green damask and red silk with appliqué embroidery.
H. 65"   W. 45½"
Italy, 17th century
Border inscription: "May He cause His face to shine toward us;
Selah" (Ps. 67.2). In central panel: (a) Crown, with the words
"Crown of the Torah." (b) Cartouche: "The Sabbath, holy unto
the Lord." (c) Cartouche: "The Lord, blessed be He." Hebrew
letters denote the year 1644.
Harry G. Friedman Collection

PLATE V

5

PLATE III   26

6

Plate IV

8. TORAH ARK CURTAIN WITH VALANCE   F 1650

Red velvet with appliqué embroidery.
Curtain: H. 92½″ W. 66″
Valance: H. 25″ W. 59″
Frankfort-on-the-Main, Germany, 1713

Torah Ark Curtain: Two twisted columns with vine and grapes; between, a rectangular panel with plant and fruit ornamentation in five horizontal and five vertical lines. Over the columns, vases with flowers. Between, two confronted rampant lions holding a crown; above it are the words "Crown of the Torah." Under the crown, the inscription "Veil of the screen before the Ark of Testimony, at the instance of Joseph, son of Hamil the Levite." At the end of the inscription, a small ewer, symbol of the Levite. Below the panel, in a cartouche, surrounded by floral designs, the date 1713.

Valance: Upper row: Three crowns, each with respective inscription underneath, "Crown of Priesthood," "Crown of Torah," "Crown of Royalty." Between middle and right crowns, inscription "Know before Whom thou standest." Between middle and left crowns, "I have set the Lord always before me" (Ps. 16.8). Lower row (right to left, with respective inscriptions): Seven-Branched Candlestick ("Menorah of Gold"); Laver ("Laver of Copper"); Tablets of the Law with Ten Commandments (the words "Two Tablets" above, "Moses" on one side, and "Our Teacher" on the other); Incense altar ("Altar of Copper"); Breastplate of the high priest with the names on the stones ("Inquire after my judgments *urim vetumim*").

The Torah Ark Curtain was originally given to a Frankfort synagogue after the great fire of 1711. In 1933 it was taken to Switzerland and then to the United States.

Harry G. Friedman Collection

---

* 9a, b. TORAH ARK CURTAIN WITH VALANCE   F 1285 a, b

Venetian red and green velvet with appliqué embroidery and brocade.
H. Curtain, 68½″ H. Valance, 37″
Southern Germany, dated 1772
Embroidered by Jacob Koppel Gans

Torah Curtain: Top: Large crown held by two griffons (superscription "Crown of the Torah"). Inscription beneath, "Jacob Kitzingen, son of Leb, and his wife, Hindel, daughter of Tebeli Ulma from Pfersee." On either side of griffons, vases with flowers. Central panel: Between two twisted columns, adorned with vines. Large Seven-Branched Candlestick on elaborate base. On either side of shaft, in large lettering, "Menorah of Gold." Between lettering and base, birds. Below panel: Double-headed eagle with crown, between heads; and cartouche with two fish between wings. Cartouche to right with date 1772 indicated by dotted letters in inscription, "And thou, Israel, my servant, Jacob whom I have chosen, the seed of Abraham my friend" (Isa. 41.8). Cartouche to left, inscription, "Work of my hands, in which I take pride, with the help of God, Jacob Koppel Gans, son of Judah Leb, 'Goldsticker' (embroiderer), Hochstadt, Bavaria."

Valance: Top, center: Double-headed eagle with scallop shell between heads and cartouche with two fish between wings. Below, inscriptions between embroidered bands, "I have set the Lord always before me" (Ps. 16.8). To left, "Know before Whom thou standest," (Talmud, Berachoth 28B). Center: Below eagle: Crown of Priesthood over a Seven-Branched Candlestick; to the right, Crown of the Torah; to the left, Crown of Royalty. At either end, a bird with lettering (abbreviated) for "Two Cherubim." (These objects are designated by Hebrew inscriptions.) Below: Scalloped border. From right to left, Tablets of the Law, and below, Ark of Covenant; Laver on triangular base, Altar of copper, and Table for the Showbread. (These objects are designated by Hebrew inscriptions.) The double-headed eagle, crown and menorah constitute a unit.

First record of this curtain is its sale at auction in New York, 1905. See: Franz Landsberger, "Old Time Torah Curtains," *Hebrew Union College Annual*, Cincinnati, O., vol. XIX, 1945-1946, pp. 353-389.

Harry G. Friedman Collection

PLATE VI

10a, b. TORAH ARK CURTAIN WITH VALANCE   F 2566 a, b

White lace.
Curtain: H. 59" W. 50" Valance: H. 17" W. 57"
Curtain: Austria (?), 18th century
Valance: Italy (?), 18th century
White curtains were for use on the High Holidays
Valance: Confronted lions, birds, rosettes

Curtain: Outer Border: Crowned double-headed eagles, confronted stags, birds, floral patterns and vases with flowers. Central panel: Floral pattern with stags and birds. Below panel: Ewer and basin (between flowers), indicating that the donor was a Levite.

Inscription on Curtain: (a) Crown of the Torah and (b) abbreviation for the phrases "Remember me," "Think of me," and "O Lord," referring to Psalms 106.4. The inscription is appropriate for the New Year as the Day of Divine Remembrance.

Harry G. Friedman Collection

*11. CENTERPIECE FROM TORAH ARK CURTAIN   JM 125-47

Silver and gold appliqué on red velvet.
H. 55½" W. 49¼"
Frankfort-on-the-Main, Germany, 1731

In center, laver indicating that the donor was a Levite. Inscription: "This belongs to . . . Lazar, the son of . . . Simon, a Levite, of Hochberg . . . and to his wife, Breinele, the daughter . . . Haim of Bamberg." Dotted letters in the inscription (Gen. 15,2), ". . . he that shall be possessor of my house is Eliezer of Damascus . . ." indicates the date 1731.

Gift of Henry L. Moses, New York City, in memory of Bernard and Johanna Moses.

PLATE VII

7

PLATE V   30

9a

9b

PLATE VI

11

PLATE VII   32

TORAH MANTLE AND WRAPPER

The Scroll is covered with a mantle, originally a wrapping of fine silk made for the protection of the scroll. In the course of time the mantle for the Torah took the form of a sheath made to fit over the scroll. In the Sephardic tradition, in which no Torah breastplate is used, the mantle is split open, thus resembling a human dress particularly when a shoulder piece is added. The mantle in the Ashkenazic tradition is open only at the bottom. The Sephardic mantle is usually made of fine brocades, the Ashkenazic mantle of embroidered velvet.

Before the mantle is pulled over the Torah the scroll is held together tightly by a ribbon. In central European countries a Torah wrapper is used for this purpose. It is a band usually about six inches in width and of sufficient length to be wound around the entire height of the parchment scroll. Sometimes the swaddling cloth used at the circumcision of a boy was cut into four parts and sewn together as a Torah wrapper. Upon the first visit of the boy to the synagogue, usually when he attained the age of four, he would bring such a wrapper to the Torah in a little ceremony which ended with the child being permitted to touch the Torah ornaments.

The wrapper bore Hebrew text giving the child's name, the date of his birth, and ending with the wish that he may grow up to study Torah, enter upon marriage, and perform good deeds. The text is put on the fabric either in embroidery or in stencil painting, both producing rather colorful effects. These Torah wrappers became in many cases the source of important information regarding the birthdates of members of congregations. It was customary to use the Torah wrapper of a particular boy on the Sabbath of his *Bar Mitzvah*, that is, when he was confirmed at the age of thirteen.

The Jewish Museum has collected many of these items, and every one consists of four pieces sewn together. In the older wrappers, those of the seventeenth and early eighteenth centuries the three seams joining the four parts are more conspicuous than in later ones. The Italian Torah wrappers show floral and other ornamentation and, in some cases, dedication inscriptions, different from the texts of the central European pieces.

*12. TORAH MANTLE   JM 5-49

> *Silver metallic thread embroidered on dark red velvet.*
> *H. 32"   W. 18"*
> *Made for synagogue of Mannheim, in 1723*
>
> Inscription: "This is the gift of . . . Bluemele, daughter of . . . Haim Winzheim . . . wife of . . . Kopel Levi of Mannheim, in the year 1723."
>
> Gift of Mrs. Maurice Weinfeld, Bronx, N. Y.
>
>   PLATE VIII

12

13

PLATE VIII   34

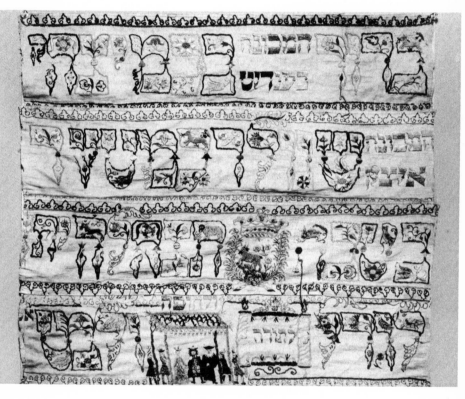

14

*13. **TORAH MANTLE** F 2634

Appliqué metallic embroidery on red velvet.
H. 35″ W. 21½″
Germany, ca. 1700
On top, the Crown of the Torah, held by lions resting on dome-shaped panel, with five bells (possibly alluding to the Five Books of Moses). For generations this mantle was in the family of Oldenburg-Goldschmidt, Altona, Germany.
Harry G. Friedman Collection

PLATE VIII

*14. **TORAH WRAPPER** D 155

Linen embroidered with silk.
Germany, 1735
Typical example of Ashkenazic work. Made for Baruch Bendit, son of Isaac Itzak. The inscription includes the prayer that the boy may grow up "to the Torah, to marriage, and to good deeds."

PLATE IX

15. **TORAH WRAPPER** F 3509

Metallic thread embroidered on silk. Ornamentation in green and silver, with yellow silk. Ground is rose; back beige.
Italy, 1712
Inscriptions: "The precepts of the Lord are right, rejoicing the heart; the commandment of the Lord is pure, enlightening the eyes" (Psalms 19.9). Gift of Hannah, wife of Baruch Luzzato, 1712. The Luzzatos were prominent scholars.

*16. **TORAH WRAPPER** S 131

White linen, embroidered in colored silk.
L. 144″ W. 7″
Germany, 1812
Human figures, plants, birds and animals; name of the boy, "Haim, son of Judah Gomperz," born in Elul (September), with the appropriate zodiac symbol of Virgo.
Benguiat Collection

PLATE X

17. **TORAH WRAPPER** F 2746

Linen, handpainted.
H. 7¾″ L. 134″
Germany, dated 1836
Decorations of floral and vine borders, and inscription, "For Nehemiah, son of Moses (Levite), born 1836."
(a) After the name of the father, Moses (Levite), is a crown over a one-handled vase set on a two-handled vase, between lions; lettering to denote Crown of Royalty. Also inscription: "This is that which belongeth unto the Levites" (Num. 8.24), an appropriate quotation for a Levitical family. Also, "And they shall wash their hands and their feet" (Ex. 40.31).
(b) After the words, "Born under a happy constellation" is a figure of a girl under a tree to denote the constellation Virgo for the month of the boy's birth.
(c) After the words, "May the Lord enable him to grow up unto the Torah," the words "Unto the Torah" are on an open

16

scroll of the Torah with the inscription "The Torah Moses commanded us." Over the scroll is a crown with the lettering "Crown
of the Torah" and alongside is Moses with the Tablets of the
Law, and above it the inscription "And Moses descended from
the mountain with the two tables of the testimony in his hand"
(Ex. 32.15).

(d) After the words "Unto marriage," there are a bride and
bridegroom holding hands, under a tree, the tree apparently
intended to serve as a canopy. The inscription alongside is "The
sound of gladness and the sound of rejoicing."

(e) After the words "And unto good deeds" there are a stag
and a lion on either side of a tree, each with the appropriate
inscription: "Fleet as a stag" and "Strong as a lion" (from the
Mishnah, Sayings of the Fathers, 4:5).

Other decorations, part of lettering, human-headed serpent

Harry G. Friedman Collection

TORAH DRESSED IN ASHKENAZIC MANNER

*18a. TORAH CROWN   S 560

Silver and silver plate, partly gilded.
H. 14¾"   D. 7½" to 8¼"
Poland, 18th century

On lower circlet, three plaques with inscriptions of the Crown
of the Torah, Crown of the Priesthood, and Crown of Royalty,
ornamented with shells and stars. Six staves ornamented with
leaves, scrolls and birds; bells between the staves. On top, small
crown with bells, surmounted by urn-shaped finial.

Felix M. Warburg Collection

PLATE XI

*18b. TORAH BREASTPLATE   S 1363 b

Silver repoussé work, partly gilt.
H. 10"   W. 7⅜"
Galicia, 1817

Center, the Tablets of the Law. To right and left of the Tablets,
the Lions of Judah. To right and left of the holiday label are
two phoenixes, leaves and scrolls. Beneath the Crown the two
blessing hands of the priest, indicating that the donor was a
Kohen. Inscription around the Tablets of the Law: "And thou
shalt make a plate of pure gold, and engrave upon it, like the
engravings of a signet: 'Holy to the Lord'" (Ex. 28.36, 27). At
side of Tablets, the priestly blessing. On the Crown the words:

"Dedicated by Elijahu, son of Rabbi Israel of sacred memory."
Gift of Max M. Karp, N. Y. C., in memory of his father, Mischa
L. Karp.

PLATE XI

*18c. TORAH MANTLE   F 875

Blue brocade and green velvet, embroidered.
H. 34"   W. 21"
Germany, 1765

Leaves and flower motifs, embroidered around inscription, "Given
by Isaac Haendle and his wife."

Harry G. Friedman Collection

PLATE XI

*18d. TORAH POINTER   S 1363 c

Silver filigree.
L. 7¾"
Galicia, early 19th century

PLATE XI

18

PLATE XI

19

*19. TORAH SCROLL JM 54-52

Torah on wooden rollers, with silver finials and handles.
H. (Scroll) 6½″   H. (Rollers) 15½″
Nuremberg, Germany, ca. 1700 (R³ 3767)
Master: ICW (Johann Conrad Weiss) (R³ 4279)

Decorations: Turned handles and finials.

Gift of Samuel Lemberg, N. Y. C.

PLATE XII

PLATE XII   40

*20. TORAH SCROLL WITH WRAPPER, MANTLE
AND POINTER   F 2925 a, b, c, d

Torah Scroll on silver rollers. Mantle, brocaded velvet.
Pointer, silver.
H. (rollers) 15¾"   H. (scroll) 7"
Austria, 18th century

Torah Scroll topped by rosebud finials. Mantle brocaded with
the Crown of the Law.

Formerly in the possession of Moritz Guedemann, Chief Rabbi
of Vienna.

Harry G. Friedman Collection

PLATE XIIA

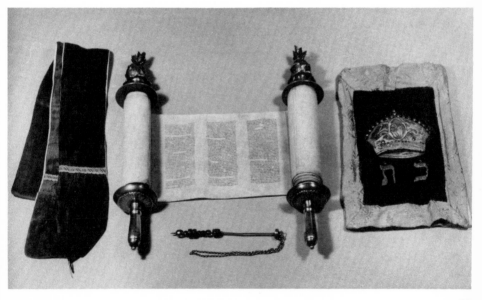

20

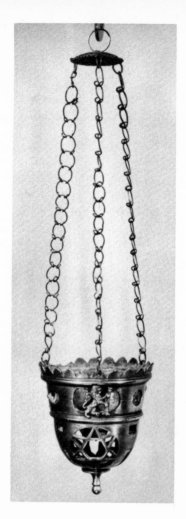

21

°21. ETERNAL LIGHT   F 3124

> *Brass, cast and cutout work.*
> *H. 6½″   D. 5½″*
> *Italy, 17th century*

Lion rampant with column and six-pointed star. The Eternal Light is suspended in front of the Torah Ark. In Eastern European synagogues it was frequently placed in special niches. Sephardic synagogues often have several. The Eternal Light can be traced to Lev. 24.2: "Command the children of Israel, that they bring unto thee pure olive oil beaten for the light, to cause a lamp to burn continually."

Harry G. Friedman Collection

PLATE XIII

PLATE XIII   42

TORAH HEADPIECES AND CROWNS

Among the silver ornaments for the Torah, the headpieces *(Rimmonim)* seem to be the oldest. *Rimmonim* is the plural of *Rimmon* which means pomegranate, a symbol of fertility and life throughout the Near East. It is easy to see that the idea of the Torah as the Tree of Life is connected with the use of the pomegranate form, as the ornamentation on the Torah rods which have the name *Etz chayim,* meaning Tree of Life. The two pillars *Yakhin* and *Boaz* of Solomonic Temple were ornamented with pomegranates, and pomegranates were also embroidered on the garb of the High Priest: "A golden bell and a pomegranate, upon the skirts of the robe round about" (Exodus 28.34). Herein undoubtedly lies the origin of the bells which are to be found on most of the *Rimmonim.*

The form of the pomegranate is more or less preserved in the various types of *Rimmonim,* although in the course of time an architectural type developed which emancipated itself from the basic round form of the original Torah headpieces. The oldest *Rimmonim* seem to be those preserved in the Cathedral of Palma di Mallorca, dating back to the fifteenth century.

Various countries have developed different forms and arrangements of the headpieces. In the Near East the original round form prevails. In Italy the traditional bells are attached with chains. In western countries the architectural influence of the tower is evident. Torah headpieces were preferred by the Sephardim to the Torah Crowns, which are more characteristic of the Ashkenazic tradition. In Italy where both traditions meet, headpieces and crowns are used together.

In northern countries there developed a custom of using the headpieces for the Sabbath and the Crowns for the Holidays. Since the latter half of the last century this usage has fallen into neglect.

Torah Crowns, while perhaps not so old as Rimmonim, are known to have existed in the Middle Ages, although none of the extant examples antedates the eighteenth century. While the Crown is modelled after certain architectural forms, it has preserved in its ornaments the wreath, which is the precursor of the Crown. This explains the frequent floral ornamentation of Torah Crowns.

°22. TORAH HEADPIECES   J 12 B

Silver, cast, with cutout and engraved decoration.
H. 22"
Mantua, Italy, 17th century
Master: SIC
Hallmark: (R³ 7391)

Outstanding example of the Italian type; perfect proportions and rich, well-balanced decoration.

Lent by Michael M. Zagayski, N. Y. C.

PLATE XIV

22

23

PLATE XIV   44

*23. TORAH HEADPIECES   F 2544

Silver, partly gilded, hammered, case and openwork.
H. 8" D. 4¼"
Poland (Lemberg?), ca. 1780
Restamping of Lemberg, 1806-07 (Beuque No. 1343)

Flattened semi-spherical base, column surmounted by floral and
fruit ornament. Bird finial. Openwork floral designs between spiral
ribbon bands. Base decorations include lion, phoenix, lamb, fox,
on leaf scrolls.

In workmanship related to Galician Torah Crown F 2585, Cat. No. 35,
Pl. XIX, Jewish Museum, N. Y. C.

Harry G. Friedman Collection

PLATE XIV

*24. TORAH HEADPIECES   F 2826 a, b

Silver, partly gilt, cast and cutout work, with semi-precious stones.
H. 26¾"
Turin, Italy (R³ 7470 with DM), late 18th century
Master: LV

Cast figures of Temple Implements. Upper row: Ark, Candelab-
rum, Altar of Burnt Offerings, Showbread, Tablets of the Law,
and blooming Staff of Aaron. Lower row: Four baskets with
first fruits, chalice for wine, and censer.

Inscription: Dedicated by Ottolenghi family, 1817.

Harry G. Friedman Collection

PLATE XV

25. TORAH HEADPIECES   F 1983 a, b

Silver, gilded.
H. 8⅜"
Nuremberg, Germany, 1695-1700

Finial, bear holding shield with engraved pitcher, symbol of the
Levite. On each lower rim are four holes, indicating that these
pieces were once nailed to the rollers of a Torah Scroll.

Harry G. Friedman Collection

*26. TORAH HEADPIECES   F 70 a, b

Silver, partly gilded.
H. 15"
Nuremberg, Germany, ca. 1720
Master: ICW (Johann Conrad Weiss) (R³ 4279)

Engraved and hammered; with gadroon and band ornamentation;
sets of six bells each, placed in arches at two levels. Finial, crown
with bell.

Harry G. Friedman Collection

PLATE XV

24

26

PLATE XV

°27. TORAH HEADPIECES   JM 19-52

Gilded silver, chased, cutout and cast.
H. 15"
Fuerth, Germany (R³ 2152), late 18th century
Master: IR (R³ 2157)

Finials: Crowns with bells and lions on top. Two-story towers with alternating pierced windows and arches with bells.
Rosenberg calls the master I. Rimmonim, (which means Torah headpieces), an improbable name, not found in the records of Fuerth.
See following pieces by the same master: Torah Pointer F 1751; Torah Breastplate JM 9-51; Kiddush Cup JM 22-52, Cat. No. 101; Jewish Museum, N. Y. C.
Gift of the Jewish Cultural Reconstruction, Inc.

PLATE XVI

°28. TORAH HEADPIECES   S 24

Wood with plaster, partly gilt.
H. 16½"
Near East, ca. 1700

Round turret form with dome and cone finial; six round arches on each tier; on round shafts with gadroon tops.
Benguiat Collection, Jewish Museum, N. Y. C.

PLATE XVI

°29. TORAH HEADPIECES   F 3685

Silver, partly gilt, repoussé and cast.
H. 17½"
Frankfort-on-the-Main, Germany
Master: IZ in oval—Jeremiah Zobel (R³ 2050), ca. 1720

Hexagonal turret form in three stories, surmounted by an open-work crown with ball finial, each tier with bells set in arches. Bowl-shaped base on tubular twisted shaft with knop on top.
By the same master: Candlestick with Spice Drawer F 2661, Cat. No. 96, PL. XLVII, Jewish Museum, N. Y. C.; also Torah Headpieces, Historical Museum, Frankfort.
Harry G. Friedman Collection

PLATE XVII

°30. TORAH HEADPIECES   L 27-51

Silver, partly gilded.
H. 8½"
Holland, 18th century
Master: LC

Round shaft on flattened bell-shaped base. Six curved brackets ending in animal heads, six bells attached. Finial: gilded crown with engraved leaf decoration and pointed terminal.
Gift of Charles M. Warburg, London, England.

PLATE XVIII

27

28

Plate XVI   48

29

PLATE XVII

30

31

PLATE XVIII 50

*31. TORAH HEADPIECES   F 2827 a, b
Silver, cast and embossed.
H. 17¼"
Amsterdam, Holland, ca. 1705 (R³ 7566)
Master: VH

Hexagonal turret form in two stories, surmounted by a crown
with spire finial; each tier with arched openings and bells, flanked
by corbels, over a base with suspended bells, on tubular shaft
with gadrooned knop at top.

Compare A. G. Grimwade, "The Original Silver of the Bevis Marks
Synagogue," *Apollo,* 1950; pp. 103-130. Also *Treasures of a London
Synagogue,* London, 1951, No. 15, Pl. XI.

Harry G. Friedman Collection

PLATE XVIII

32. TORAH HEADPIECE (One of Pair)   F 3068
Silver, repoussé and cast.
H. 15½"
Venice, Italy, 17th century (R³ 7485 and R³ 7486 with letters RP)

Hexagonal body with canopy; vase and flower finial, sides
adorned with bouquets of flowers. Long shaft on conical base
with repoussé ornaments. S-shaped lower ornaments. Balustrades.
Inscriptions: "From Judica Levia, to be used on the scroll for
Kol Nidre (eve of the Day of Atonement) every year." Also,
"Holy unto the Lord."

33. TORAH HEADPIECES   F 3281
Silver, cast.
H. 17"
Amsterdam, Holland, late 17th century

Hexagonal turret form; openwork crown with cone finial, resting
on a dome over four stories having arches with suspended bells,
each stage enriched by a delicate gallery; on tubular shaft with
central gadrooned knop.

Compare almost identical pair of headpieces in the Amsterdam Portu-
guese Synagogue, dated 1751, but apparently of earlier origin; *Hebrew
Union College Bulletin,* April 1945; note by Franz Landsberger.

Harry G. Friedman Collection

34. TORAH HEADPIECES   F 3283
Silver.
H. 7½"
Persia, 18th century

The spherical form suggests the pomegranate (Rimmon). Orien-
tal type, bottom slanted to fit over rollers of Near-Eastern silver
Torah case. Bells suspended by chains from upper part of Headpieces.

See Torah Crown F 2585, Cat. No. 35, Pl. XIX, Jewish Museum,
N. Y. C.

Harry G. Friedman Collection

*35. TORAH CROWN   F 2585

*Silver, partly gilt, repoussé and cast work with two rows of bells,
and semi-precious stones.*
H. 19"   D. 8½" to 8¾"
Poland, 2nd half of 18th century
Tax exemption stamp of Lemberg, 1809

Decorations: Upper: Arches and pilasters, between them the
crowned double eagle, lion, stag, rabbit, griffon and another
eagle. Lower: Dome, with floral designs and animals.
Inscriptions: Cartouches with name of donor: Moses, son of Isaac
Menkes and his wife, Rachel; and two dates, one 1765, the other
probably 1774. Also the names of the parents of the donor and
his wife; quotations from Exodus 17.11, and the Sayings of the
Fathers 4.17.

Compare with Torah Headpieces F 2544, Cat. No. 23, Pl. XIV, and
F 3283, Cat. No. 34; Jewish Museum, N. Y. C. See "A Polish Torah
Crown," by Stephen S. Kayser, *HUC Annual*, vol. XVIII, Part 2, Cin-
cinnati, Ohio, 1950-1951, pp. 493 ff.

Harry G. Friedman Collection
                                                         PLATE XIX

*36. TORAH CROWN   F 3688

Silver, repoussé, with gilded decorations.
H. 7⅛"   E. 7¾"
Italy, 17th century
Master: I

Cylinder form with ten scallops forming upper rim. Scroll-work
and shell forms attached to cartouches in gilded reliefs: The Ark
of the Covenant with two wings of the cherubs; Tablets of the
Law; Censer; Mitre of the High Priest; Laver of the Levites.
Inscription in four of the five cartouches on lower band: "Ezriel
Hai, son of Rabbi Yedidiah Hai from Cinto (near Ferrara)."

The cylinder form of the Italian Torah Crowns comes from the practice
of putting the crown on the Torah Scroll together with Headpieces.

Harry G. Friedman Collection
                                                         PLATE XX

*37. TORAH CROWN   F 3131

Silver and silver filigree on gilded brass base.
H. 8½"
Warsaw (?), Poland, 1840-1850

Crown with six bells and eagle finial, on a hexagonal gilded brass
base with filigree overlay.
Inscription: "Bezalel donated this Crown of the Torah in memory
of . . . Jacob . . . the son-in-law of the Gaon Akiba Eger . . ."
For same type of filigree compare Spice Container F 2372, Jewish
Museum, N. Y. C.

Harry G. Friedman Collection
                                                         PLATE XX

35

PLATE XIX

36

37

PLATE XX

54

°38. TORAH CROWN JM 15-52

Silver, originally partly gilded, repoussé, cast and openwork.
H. 7½" D. (lower) 9½" D. (upper) 11½"
Nuremberg, Germany, ca. 1715
Master: Indistinct mastermark—bird.

Upper part older. Crown in Louis XIV style with staves upholding small crown finial; lower part, circular band with Regency
decoration. Formerly in the synagogue of Friedberg (Hesse).

Compare R. Hallo, "Juedische Kunst aus Hessen und Nassau," Berlin,
1933, No. 16; R. Hallo, *Notizblaetter der Gesellschaft zur Erforschung
Juedischer Kunstdenkmaeler* No. 23, page 1; E. Moses, "Aus der
Geschichte der Juden im Rheinland," *Juedische Kult-und Kunstdenkmaeler*, Duesseldorf, 1931, p. 154.

PLATE XXI

39. TORAH CROWN F 268

Silver, partly gilded, cast and cutout work.
H. 9¾" D. 5½"
Poland (Krakow ?), ca. 1810

Strapwork ornamentation on lower crown. Six staves held by
lions support a small upper crown with bulb and cone finial.
Birds on upper and lower crown and on staves. Leaves and six
bells. Six blue circular semi-precious stones.

See Spice Container JM 34-51, Cat. No. 91, Pl. XLV, and D 53;
Jewish Museum, N. Y. C.

Harry G. Friedman Collection

TORAH BREASTPLATE AND POINTER

The origin of the Torah breastplate has been dealt with briefly in the introduction. Because of its shape the breastplate gave the silversmith ample scope for ornamental compositions. The interchangeable plates, indicating the various occasions for which the Torah was used, are found in practically all of the old pieces except for the very small ones. They indicate the practical origin of the breastplate.

As an ornamental item the breastplate assumes special significance since it is related to the *Hoshen*, the breastplate of the biblical High Priest, which was studded with stones of various colors—twelve of them, for the Tribes of Israel. Some breastplates actually use semi-precious stones.

The Torah pointer (in Hebrew, *Yad*, meaning hand) is used, because one should not touch the sacred scroll with the bare fingers in following the lines of the text while it is read. There are no known medieval specimens of pointers, nor are there any references to Torah pointers before the late 16th century. The pointers are ordinarily made of silver and in most of them the rod ends in the representation of a human hand, usually the right hand, but occasionally they are shaped after the left human hand. Sometimes a ring with a small semi-precious stone appears on the pointing finger. A special group of specimens has the motif of a fish out of which stretches a hand holding another hand. The fish comes into the ornamentation of the Torah pointer because the Torah is likened to water, the element of the fish.

*40. TORAH BREASTPLATE   F 3053
Silver, partly gilt, repoussé and cast work.
H. 10⅛″ W. 8″
Nuremberg, Germany, 1630-1640 (R³ 3765)
Master: GB (perhaps Georg Bang) (R³ 4200)
The columns of the Temple, surmounted by lions, upholding the Crown of the Torah; in center, the Seven-Branched Candlestick. On the pendants, added later, a dedication inscription of 1746. Cf. Torah Pointer F 878, Cat. No. 64, Pl. XXXII, Jewish Museum, N. Y. C.
Harry G. Friedman Collection

PLATE XXII

*41. TORAH BREASTPLATE   F 2653
Silver, engraved.
H. 4½″ W. 5½″
Bohemia, 1669
Simple rectangular plate with engraved border and raised edge, similarly ornamented rectangle in center with the words "Holy Sabbath." Main inscription: "The child Uriel, son of Ezriel, born . . . on the 9th day of Sivan, 1669. May God enable him to grow up unto Torah, Huppah, and good deeds."
Formerly in the Collection of Gustav G. Gumpel, San Francisco, Cal.
Harry G. Friedman Collection

PLATE XXII

42. TORAH BREASTPLATE   M 8
Silver, repoussé work with semi-precious stones.
H. 10¾″ W. 11½″
Probably Augsburg, Germany, end of 17th century
Hallmarks and mastermarks missing, perhaps because part of the edge is broken away.

40

41

57   PLATE XXII

°43. TORAH BREASTPLATE   F 248
Silver and gilt, repoussé work.
H. 9¼" W. 9¼"
Augsburg, Germany, 1695-1700 (R³ 191)
Master: DS—Dominicus Saler (1718) (R³ 788)
Columns of the Temple, Crown of the Torah, garlands of acanthus
leaves and flowers.
Harry G. Friedman Collection

PLATE XXIII

°44. TORAH BREASTPLATE   F 740
Silver, cast, openwork.
H. 6¼" W. 9¼"
Frankfort-on-the-Main, Germany, ca. 1710 (R³ 2004)
Master: IMS—Johann Matthias Sandrat (R³ 2055)

Raised columns and Crown of the Law on a broad rectangular
field with a baroque border. Scrolls with grapevine ornamentation.

Compare with Breastplate in Cluny Museum, Paris, No. 26, M. Strauss
Collection; also catalogue, Anglo-Jewish Historical Exhibition, London,
1887, No. 1459.

Harry G. Friedman Collection

PLATE XXIV

°45. TORAH BREASTPLATE   F 3686
Silver, partly gilt, repoussé and cast work.
H. 10½" W. 12"
Nuremberg, Germany, ca. 1700 (R³ 3761)
Master: R (perhaps Thomas Ringler) (R³ 4246)

Cast figures, embossed grapevine and acanthus. Principal details:
(a) Crowned double-headed eagle; (b) Crown of the Law between two lions; (c) long rectangular frame for individual letters
to indicate the Sabbath or holidays, set between lions; (d) confronted unicorns; (e) above the rectangular frame, a medallion
with a ewer (symbol of the Levite) and the inscription "Naphtali
Hirsch Segal" (abbreviation for Levite); (f) below the rectangular form, a medallion with the inscription "Zira, daughter of
Raphael," surrounding the zodiac symbol, Gemini.

Harry G. Friedman Collection

PLATE XXIV

°46. TORAH BREASTPLATE   L 84-48
Silver with appliqué ornaments, cutout and cast work.
H. 9½" W. 9"

Two cutout lions holding cast appliqué of Crown of the Torah;
shell and acanthus scrolls. Pitcher added, indicating donor was
a Levite. Indicator for Sabbath and holidays, in trefoil border.

Rudolph Hallo, Catalogue of Marburg, No. 19; Elizabeth Moses,
Juedische Kult-und Kunstdenkmaeler in den Rheinlandern, Rheinscher
Verein Fuer Denkmalpflege und Heimatschutz, 1951, vol. 1, pp.
150-152, published in Dusseldorf.

PLATE XXV

43

PLATE XXIII

44

45

PLATE XXIV   60

46

47

PLATE XXV

°47. TORAH BREASTPLATE   F 70-3
Silver gilt, repoussé work.
H. 13¾"   W. 12"
Augsburg, Germany, ca. 1725 (R³ 230)
Master: ZW
Crown of the Law resting on two rampant lions with averted
heads. One lion holding a laver, the other a basin, to indicate
that the donor was a Levite. Four columns in two connected
pairs to indicate the Holy of Holies. In center, two shell patterns
with rectangle for Sabbath and festival indicators. Below, a table
with vase of flowers. All-over ornaments of grapevines and fes-
toons. Gadroon border.
See Torah Pointer F 70-4, Cat. No. 63, Pl. XXXII.
Harry G. Friedman Collection

PLATE XXV

°48. TORAH BREASTPLATE   S 34
Silver, partly gilded, repoussé work.
H. 10¾"   W. 10¾"
Augsburg, Germany, 1700-1710 (R³ 192)
Master: MW (Markus or Matthews Wolff) (R³ 726)
The Jewish Museum, N. Y. C., has Torah breastplate, JM 30-52, by
the same master; also spice container, JM 35-52, Cat. No. 86, Pl.
XLIII. See also Torah Headpieces J 16 in the Michael M. Zagayski
Collection, N. Y. C.; and breastplate in the Karl Schwarz Collection,
Tel Aviv, Israel, formerly in the synagogue of Augsburg, Germany.

PLATE XXVI

°49. TORAH BREASTPLATE   M 206
Silver, repoussé and engraved.
Poland, 1780
H. 8¼"   W. 8"
Tendrils frame Tablets of the Law and inscription: "Crown of
Torah. This breastplate belongs to . . . Meir, son of . . . David
. . . year 1780."

PLATE XXVII

°50. TORAH BREASTPLATE   L 19-54
Silver, repoussé.
H. 10½"   W. 11"
Augsburg, Germany, 1750
Master: IW
Moses with staff to left; Aaron with censer to right; between,
crown finial over a valance-like hanging with five tassels to suggest the Five Books of Moses. Frame for movable indicators for
the Sabbath and Holidays. Hands of priest in blessing to signify
that the donor was a Kohen (descendent of the ancient priesthood).
Motif of Moses and Aaron is taken from engraved title pages of
Hebrew books; for example, the Bible printed in Amsterdam, in
1679. See also Breastplate M 293, Cat. No. 51, Pl. XXVIII. The
same motif appears in Breastplates from Breslau; a notable example is in the Jewish collection of the University of Boston.
Compare: Stephen S. Kayser; "Ein Seltenes Thoraschild," in *Bulletin
of Congregation Beth Hillel*, N. Y. C., No. 100, 1952, p. 14.
Lent by Beth Hillel Congregation, N. Y. C.

PLATE XXVII

48

63   PLATE XXVI

49

50

PLATE XXVII 64

*51. TORAH BREASTPLATE   M 293

Silver, repoussé work.
H. 12"   W. 9½"
Breslau, Germany, 1720

The Tablets of the Law surmounted by cartouche with the name of God, to which Moses (right) points. Aaron (left) holds the censer. Decoration in baroque form; five shells on upper parts. Inscription: "Holy to the Lord . . . Presented by Benjamin, son of Gerson . . . and his pious wife Sheine Reisl, daughter of Abraham."

Compare with Augsburg Breastplate S 34, Cat. No. 48, Pl. XXVI, Jewish Museum, N. Y. C.

PLATE XXVIII

*52. TORAH BREASTPLATE   L 9-54

Silver.
H. 16"   W. 12"
Nuremberg, Germany, ca. 1700
Master: Hahn (?)
Mastermark: Rooster

Upper part: Center, crown, angels on ladder (Jacob's Dream). Right, Moses receiving the Tablets of the Law on Mount Sinai (Shabuoth). Left, booths and men (Succoth). Middle part: Indicator for Sabbaths and holidays in rectangle, between twisted columns. Niche to right, vase and flowers; inscription (Gen. 22.3). Similar niche to left with inscription, (Gen. 24.63). Lower part: Right, Passover scene as described in Ex. 12.11 (Passover). Left, group with man blowing shofar (Rosh Hashanah). Center, Levite with basin to left, and Kohen (priest) to right. Inscription, (Num. 8.24), "This is that pertaineth unto the Levites," indicates the owner was a Levite.

Lent by Irving Lehman Collection, Temple Emanu-El, N. Y. C.

PLATE XXVIII

*53. TORAH BREASTPLATE   F 2546

Silver, partly gilt, repoussé and cast.
H. 8½"   W. 6"
Poland, 1766
Master: Ze'eb (i.e., Wolf), son of A (Abraham ?)
Hallmark: Pietrokov

Griffons on columns hold crown placed over Tablets of the Law.

Cartouche (above rectangle with indicator for the Sabbath and holidays) with inscription "Belongs to the Society for Study of the Bible." Inscription on the lower edge reads: "This is the work of my hands in which I take pride. Ze'eb, son of Abraham (?) silversmith from Pietrokov in the year 1766." Rare example of an 18th century Eastern European Jewish silversmith's work with maker's name.

Harry G. Friedman Collection

PLATE XXIX

51

52

PLATE XXVIII   66

53

54

PLATE XXIX

55

PLATE XXX   68

*54. TORAH BREASTPLATE   F 996 a
Silver and gilt.
H. 17″   W. 12″
Probably Wuerzburg, Germany, ca. 1740
Mastermark: No hallmark or other identification, but accompany-
ing Torah pointer has hallmark of Wuerzburg, 1740
Crown of the Torah above Tablets of the Law between cherub
wings; below, rectangle for the Sabbath and festival indicators;
right, Table of Showbread; left, the Menorah; on lower register
from right to left, sunrise, altar of incense with flames, cartouche
with lettering, ewer, crescent moon with six stars. Inscription on
two cartouches below. Inscription: "Presented by Joshua Samuel
Kolin (?) from Heitzfeld and his wife Gittel. In the year 1742."
Harry G. Friedman Collection

PLATE XXIX

*55. TORAH BREASTPLATE   F 2280
Silver, partly gilt, repoussé with agate and carnelian stones and
gold decoration.
H. 12½″   W. 8½″
Poland, (Lemberg ?), second half of 18th century

Restamped Lemberg, 1806-07, on restored edge, (Beugue 1343)
Master: BT in shield. (Uncertain whether this is the master of the
original piece or of the restoration).
In center, Tablets of the Law. To the right and left the symbols
of the Twelve Tribes. The abbreviations of the carved carnelian
stones, "Crown of Torah," "Crown of Priesthood," "Crown of
Royalty," and above "Crown of a Good Name." The original
curved edge was destroyed and replaced in 1801.
Harry G. Friedman Collection

PLATE XXX

56. TORAH BREASTPLATE   JM 25-52
Silver, repoussé work.
H. 10½″   W. 8½″
Fuerth, Germany, 1798 (R³ 2152)
Columns of the Temple with the Lions of Judah holding the
Crown of Torah above the seven-branched candlestick and the
Tablets of the Law. See description Cat. No. 27.

57a. TORAH BREASTPLATE   F 1903
Silver, partly gilt, repoussé and openwork.
H. 5½″   W. 4½″
Poland or Moravia, 1779
Gilded Torah Ark with doors (inside small gilded scroll) between
two gilded columns with crown capitals above. Crown held by
two gilded rampant lions. Below, two confronted stags. Cartouche
without inscription, probably erased.
Belongs to Torah Crown F 1904, Cat. No. 57b, and Torah Pointer
F 1905, Cat. No. 57c. Related pieces, perhaps from same workshop,
are Breastplates M 6 and M 456, Jewish Museum, N. Y. C.
Harry G. Friedman Collection

57b. TORAH CROWN   F 1904
*Silver, hammered and gilded openwork on silver background,
with semi-precious stones.*
H. 7″   D. 3½″ to 4½″
Poland or Moravia, 1779
Finial crown on a larger crown, set in a circular band. On lower
band, Crown of Torah, Crown of Priesthood, and Crown of
Royalty. Inscription on upper crown: "This crown belongs to
. . . David, son of Jeruham. . . ."
Belongs to Torah Breastplate F 1903, Cat. No. 57a, and Torah Pointer
F 1905, Cat. No. 57c.
Harry G. Friedman Collection

57c. TORAH POINTER   F 1905
Silver and silver filigree, partly gilded.
L. 8¼″
Poland or Moravia, 1779
Dated by donor inscription, 1779
Belongs to Torah Crown F 1903, Cat. No. 57a, and Torah Breastplate
F 1904, Cat. No. 57c.
Harry G. Friedman Collection

*58. TORAH POINTER   F 2590
Silver, cast.
L. 6¼″
Galicia, ca. 1810
Harry G. Friedman Collection

                                                      PLATE XXXI

*59. TORAH POINTER   F 2751
Carved bone.
L. 7⅛″
Italy, early 19th century
*Name of donor, Yom Tob Kimhi, a member of the distinguished
family*
Harry G. Friedman Collection

                                                      PLATE XXXI

*60. TORAH POINTER   L 4-48
Silver, gilded, cast and chased.
L. 14½″
Italy, Modena (?), ca. 1700 (related to R³ 7396)
Master: GB
Inscription: Presented to the Italian synagogue by Esther Camio
in the year, 1804.
Lent by the American Joint Distribution Committee, N. Y., to
which it was presented by the Italian Jewish community.
                                                      PLATE XXXI

*61. TORAH POINTER   F 934
Silver and coral, with amethyst and turquoise stones.
L. 8¾″
Near East, 18th century
Harry G. Friedman Collection

                                                      PLATE XXXI

58

59

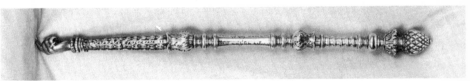

60

61

71   PLATE XXXI

62

63

64

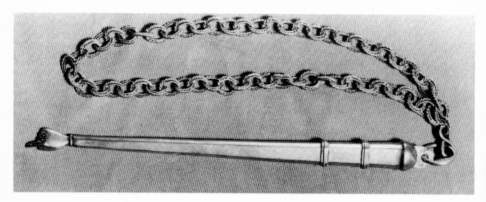

65

Plate XXXII

72

*62. TORAH POINTER WITH HOOK   F 3665
Silver
L. 8½″
Amsterdam, Holland, ca. 1762
Master: T.I.C. (?) Hallmark: Amsterdam (R³ 7567)
Hook for hanging pointer on breastplate is typically Dutch Ash-
kenazic. Inscribed with names of eight donors on octagonal shaft.
Harry G. Friedman Collection
                                                      PLATE XXXII

*63. TORAH POINTER   F 70-4
Silver, partly gilt.
L. 8½″
Augsburg, Germany, 1725 (R³ 230)
Master: CW
Belongs with Torah Breastplate F 70-3, Cat. No. 47, Pl. XXV.
Harry G. Friedman Collection
                                                      PLATE XXXII

*64. TORAH POINTER   F 878
Silver, formerly gilded.
L. 8¾″
Nuremberg, Germany, late 18th century
*Hallmark: N (R³ 3767) Master's Mark: Coat of arms showing fig-
ure of a bird, probably a stork, facing left*
Tapering rectangular shaft with cut corners. Two profiled rings
on the upper end of the shaft. End piece in form of a half sphere,
above a small trefoil to which a ring and chain are attached.
Compare JM 9-52 (Crown from Schnaittach); Torah Breastplate
F 3042 (Hallmark R³ 4295); Torah Headpieces F 3043 a, b, Cat. No.
40, Pl. XXII; Jewish Museum, N. Y. C.
Harry G. Friedman Collection
                                                      PLATE XXXII

*65. TORAH POINTER   F 3518
Silver.
L. 10¾″
Western Europe, 18th century
Twisted, tapered shaft engraved with flowers and leaves, inter-
rupted by flattened bulbs. Hand holds tiny pointer. A crown at
upper end.
Harry G. Friedman Collection
                                                      PLATE XXXII

66. TORAH POINTER   JM 47-52
Silver, with cast decorations.
L. (with ring) 11¾″
Frankfort-on-the-Main, Germany, ca 1700 (R³ 2007)
Most probably from the Old Synagogue of Frankfort.

67. TORAH POINTER   JM 48-52
Silver, cast.
L. 10¾″
Frankfort-on-the-Main (?), Germany, inscription date 1688
Perhaps originally from the Old Synagogue of Frankfort.
Gift of the Jewish Cultural Reconstruction, Inc.

SABBATH

The Protestant theologian and Orientalist, George Ewald (1803-1875), has said: "The Sabbath was something quite new, which had never before existed in any nation or in any religion—a standing reminder that man can emancipate himself from the slavery of his worldly cares; that man was made for spiritual freedom, peace, and joy."

The Sabbath, one of Israel's most important gifts to civilization, is the source of profound beauty in the Jewish home. It is inaugurated by the kindling of the Sabbath lights which, since ancient times, has been one of the most important duties of the Jewish woman. Oil was used for this ceremony until the eighteenth century, particularly in western countries. There the typical star-shaped Sabbath lamp became a mark of the Jewish home to such an extent that it was called *Judenstern* (Jewish Star). The old sources, discussing the fuel to be used for the Sabbath lights, speak mainly of the oil and the wick; but they also refer to candles, which were known as early as the second century of the common era. During the last two hundred years candles have become *the* Sabbath lights, so that the Sabbath and festival lamp has gradually disappeared as a home fixture. The candleholders used for the Sabbath lights are in many cases a precious heirloom of the family.

After the kindling of the lights, the holiness of the Sabbath is proclaimed by the *Kiddush* (Sanctification), which consecrates life in the Jewish home. During the Middle Ages this ceremony made its way into the synagogue as well. The *Kiddush* consists of two blessings: one on the holiness of the Sabbath, the other over a cup of wine.

The Bible recognizes the joyful effect of wine, ". . . that maketh glad the heart of man," (Psalm 104.15), yet the importance of wine in connection with the sanctification of the Sabbath and the festivals is of post-biblical origin. We note from the story told in the 35th chapter of Jeremiah that the drinking of wine in the Temple of biblical times was forbidden. The expression used in Psalm 23, "My cup runneth over," evidently means good fortune. The cups shown on the ancient Jewish coins of the time of Simon Maccabee and on later shekels are evidently not drinking vessels, but represent those which were used for the sacrifices in the Temple.

The custom of reciting the *Kiddush* was known at the time of the sage Hillel, about the middle of the first century B.C.E. The cup used for the *Kiddush* wine should be perfect and it is not usable if it shows any damage, particularly to the rim. This requirement, and the solemnity of the recital of the *Kiddush*, led to the use of silver as the preferred metal for *Kiddush* cups. There are also cups of other metals, and of glass. Most silver *Kiddush* cups have the form of an inverted dome, preferably with a stem and base.

It became customary to put inscriptions on the *Kiddush* cup, usually biblical quotations referring to the Sabbath or the festivals, the blessing over the wine, or even the entire *Kiddush* text. The name of the owner or, in the case of cups donated to the synagogue, the name of the donor, was also engraved.

After the *Kiddush*, the blessing over the two Sabbath loaves, is said; then the actual meal begins. Special plates and embroidered covers are used for the Sabbath breads, which remain covered during the recital of the *Kiddush*.

68

69

75   Plate XXXIII

°68. SABBATH LAMP   JM 19-53

Silver, chased and engraved.
H. (with chain) 21½" D. 11"
Italy, late 16th century
Master: SB (?)
Hallmarks: Uncertain (Type R³ 7422 Pauda) (Type R³ 1366
Breslau)

Engraved decorations, acanthus leaves, fruit and scrolls, of Renaissance character, including the putti beads ornamenting links in
the four chains. Inscriptions on each of four cartouches: (1) "The
light of God is the soul of man." (Prov. 20.27) (2) "Honor the
Lord with light." (Isa. 24.15) (3) "For the commandment is a
lamp . . ." and (4) ". . . the teaching is light." (Prov. 6.23).
Pendant apparently of a later date.

Gift of Frederick W. Seckel, N. Y. C.

                                                   PLATE XXXIII

°69. SABBATH LAMP   F 2299

Silver, repoussé, cast.
Italy, mid-18th century
Master: GAG and FIV
Hallmark: Standing female figure

Canopy-like top over bowl for oil. Lamp suspended by four chains
from canopy with tassel trim. Twelve oil burners. Elaborate floral
ornaments and ornate drip bowl. Decorations: Abraham with
Isaac on the altar; Jacob holding a ladder with angels; Samson
with jaw bone and the gates of Gaza; Moses with the Tablets of
the Law; Aaron with the Ephod and ewer; David playing harp;
Solomon with sword and scales of justice. Inscription: "Lamp for
Sabbaths and holidays 1803."

Harry G. Friedman Collection

                                                   PLATE XXXIII

°70. SABBATH LAMP (FRAGMENT)   F 2707

Silver, cast, hammered and cutout work.
H. 10"
Frankfort-on-the-Main, Germany, 1650-1670
Mastermark: SV (perhaps Valentine Schueler)

General form is a fountain, perhaps referring to Ps. 36.10: "For
with Thee is the fountain of life, in Thy light do we see light."
The statuettes hold objects associated with the Sabbath and holidays. Sabbath is indicated by a spice tower; Purim by an Esther
scroll; Passover by a matzah and matzah baking tool; Shabuoth

by the Tablets of the Law; Rosh Hashanah by a book and a trumpet (latter in lieu of a shofar); Day of Atonement by a knife, and a rooster; Sukkoth by a palm branch (Lulab) and a citrus fruit (Ethrog); the seventh day of Sukkoth (Hosha'anah Rabbah) by a willow branch. The knight in center of group is perhaps intended for Judah Maccabee, symbolizing Hanukkah. (See illustration 70a for detail.)

From the same master as the Hanukkah Lamp in the Historic Museum of Frankfort. Also from the Zagayski Collection, Hanukkah Lamp L 18-54, Cat. No. 128, Pl. LXIII; and Sabbath Lamp JM 37-52, Cat. No. 71, Pl. XXXV, formerly in Jewish Museum of Frankfort; Jewish Museum, N. Y. C. Recently the Jewish Museum in Cincinnati, O., acquired a Sabbath Lamp by the same master. For details see Guido Schoenberg, "A Silver Sabbath Lamp from Frankfort-on-the-Main" *Essays in Honor of George Swarzenski*, Berlin and Chicago, 1951, p. 189. (See illustration 70a for detail.)

Harry G. Friedman Collection

PLATE XXXIV

*71. SABBATH AND FESTIVAL LAMP   JM 37-52

Silver, with cast, cutout and engraved ornaments.
H. 22¼"
Frankfort-on-the-Main, Germany, 1680
Master: VS (Valentine Schueler ?) (R³ 1999 or R³ 2004)

Star-shaped lamp in form of fountain (like F 2707, Cat. No. 72, Pl. XXXVII). Statuettes between columns hold objects associated with the Sabbath and the festivals. The Sabbath is indicated by a candle and twisted taper (Habdalah); New Year (Rosh Hashanah), shofar and book of life; Day of Atonement (Yom Kippur), rooster and knife; Feast of Booths (Sukkoth), Lulab and Ethrog; Feast of Rededication (Hanukkah), Menorah and oil jar; Purim, Purim hammer and Esther scroll; Passover, matzah and matzah-baking tool; Feast of Weeks (Shabuoth), Tablets of the Law. The statuettes carrying festival signs were originally standard figurines wearing Spanish dress and armor, Jewish hats typical of the time being added. Drip bowl missing.

In 1903, the lamp was converted into an Eternal Light by Matilda von Rothschild in memory of her husband, Wilhelm von Rothschild. The dedication appears in Hebrew on the two flags held by the finial lion.

Other decorative motifs consist of eagle, stag, pelican and squirrel —also eight bells, and masks between fountain spouts. Top finial in form of lion, holding flags with inscription. (See illustration 71a for detail.)

For other work of same master see Sabbath Lamp F 2707, Cat. No. 70, Pl. XXIV; Hanukkah Lamp L 18-54, Cat. No. 128, Pl. LXIII, Zagayski Collection, Jewish Museum, N. Y. C.

PLATE XXXV

70

70a (detail of 70)

PLATE XXXIV 78

71

71a (detail of 71)

PLATE XXXV

*72. SABBATH AND FESTIVAL LAMP   L 10-54

Silver, with cast, cutout and engraved ornamentation.
H. 30" (top of ring to bottom of drip bowl)   D. 13"
Frankfort-on-the-Main, Germany, late 17th century
Master: Johann Adam Boller

Cylindrical tower; star-shaped eight-pointed oil lamp with inverted bell-shaped drip cup. Base in two stages, with cutout
branch decorations, lower stage a hunting scene with deer, hunter
and dog. Upper stage recessed and surrounded by a low delicate
gallery with birds in branch decorations. On base, between
twisted columns, eight statuettes holding objects associated with
the Sabbath and festivals: Sabbath night, spice tower and box
for Habdalah ceremony (this figure appears twice); Feast of
Rededication (Hanukkah), Menorah and oil jar; Purim, Purim
hammer and Esther scroll; Passover, matzah and matzah-baking
tool. The functions of the other figures are not clear, as parts are
missing. Bells are suspended above the statuettes.

The three stages above have balconies. On the lowest stand four
watchmen with lances. On the middle balcony are four figures:
Moses with an open Torah Scroll, David with a harp; the symbols
for the other two are missing. On the top balcony are four trum-
peters. The dome is surmounted by a large figure holding an
empty basket. Upper part of tower and dome have branch and
bird decorations. Middle gallery has five brackets with candleholders—a later addition. Drip cup is also of a later date.

Lent by Temple Emanu-El, N. Y. C.

                                              PLATE XXXVI

*73. SABBATH LAMP   F 2257

Silver, partly gilt.
H. 34"   D. 10½"
Hallmark: Group R³ 7566 ff.
Master: OK
Yearmark F: 1765 or 1800; Provincemark R³ 7538

Typical Sephardic Sabbath lamp used in Holland. Open oil container for seven wicks with hook, knop and crown above. Underneath, a drip bowl with knop at base.
Cf. R. Hallo, Cat. No. 32, p. 10.

Harry G. Friedman Collection

                                              PLATE XXXVII

*74. SABBATH LAMP   F 3073

Brass, cast.
H. 24"   W. (of star) 11½"
Germany, early 18th century
Lamp with eight burners, heavy shaft, decorative hook and orig-
inal channels leading to drip cup.
Harry G. Friedman Collection

                                              PLATE XXXVII

80

72

     Plate XXXVI

73

74

PLATE XXXVII   82

*75. PAIR OF SABBATH CANDLESTICKS   F 1847 a,b

Silver.
H. 9"
Germany, 18th century (?)
Marks uncertain

Bell-shaped base with three cartouches between floral and volute ornaments. Superimposed platform on which a rampant lion holds a bobeche on a branch with leaves and flowers. Scenes on base: (a) Sacrifice of Isaac; Judgment of Solomon; Woman Blessing the Sabbath Lights. (b) Jacob's Dream; Moses Tending the Sheep; Samson and the Lion.

Harry G. Friedman Collection

PLATE XXXVIII

*76. TABLECLOTH FOR FESTIVALS   S 1351

White cotton with blue and red embroidery.
L. 72" W. 68"
Roumania, 18th century

Fine specimen of Eastern European Jewish folk art. In center, text of the Kiddush (Sanctification) for the Three Festivals, above which is a crown. At corners, winged angel-heads. Eight floral ornaments are placed within the border.

PLATE XXXVIII

*77. TABLECLOTH FOR SABBATH   F 512

Silk embroidery.
D. 40"
Buchara, Persia, 18th century

Quotations from Sayings of the Fathers, the talmudic tractate from which chapters are read on summer Sabbath afternoons.

Harry G. Friedman Collection

PLATE XXXIX

*78. COVER FOR FESTIVALS   F 3596

Sheer white linen, with colored embroidered flower decorations.
L. 52" W. 24"
Austria, 18th century

Hand with pitcher in cartouche indicates owner was a Levite. Decorative motifs: Mitre of the High Priest; Libation Vessel; Censer; Hands of the Priest; Seven-Branched Candlestick; Tablets of the Law.

Inscriptions: Blessing over the wine and quotation from Lev. 23.4: "These are the appointed seasons of the Lord, even holy convocations, which ye shall proclaim in their appointed season." Formerly in the Flueckselig Collection, Vienna, Austria.

Harry G. Friedman Collection

PLATE XXXIX

75

76

PLATE XXXVIII   84

77

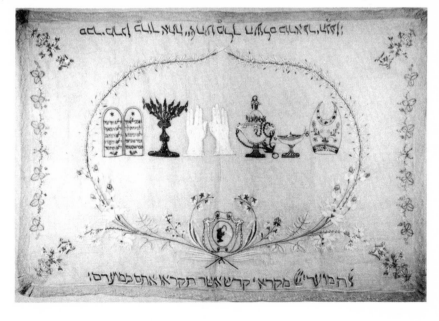

78

לֹ הַמִּשְׁרָ שׁ מִקְרָא קֹדֶשׁ אֲשֶׁר תִּקְרְאוּ אֹתָם בְּמוֹעֲדָם

80

81

PLATE XL 86

79. KIDDUSH CUP   F 221

Silver, traces of original gilding.
H. 6⅛" x 4⅛"
Augsburg, ca. 1695
Mastermark: horseshoe, R³ 606

On low base with hammered design on lower part. Inscription:
"A pure vessel, presented by the heads of the Jewish congregation, the officers of the holy community of Mayence, as a gift on
the occasion of his learned address on the Sabbath on which the
first portion of Genesis is read." Date of inscription, 1758.
It was customary for a bridegroom to deliver a learned address on the
Sabbath preceding his wedding. Hence the term "sermon present" for
wedding gift, as used in the above inscription.

Harry G. Friedman Collection

*80. KIDDUSH CUP   L 15-54

Glass tumbler with enamel decorations.
H. 3⅞"   D. 2⅝"
Austria, dated 1815
Redecorated in Vienna
Maker: AK (Anton Kothgasser)

Enamelled in black with verses from Gen. 2.1-3, and blessings
for wine and the Sabbath; a forget-me-not in color (and a fly on
reverse). Inscription below, 1815.

Lent by Jerome Strauss, N. Y. C.

PLATE XL

*81. WINE GOBLET   L 16-54

Glass, etched.
H. 6½"   D. (bowl), Rim. 2⅝"   Base 3¼"
England, ca. 1770

Inscription just below upper rim, based on Kings I. 1.34: "Long
live King Solomon," (perhaps referring to owner's name). Below
the floral decoration, inscription from Ps. 92.13, "The righteous
shall flourish like the palm tree, he shall grow tall like a cedar in
Lebanon." From Zech. 8.12, "The vine shall give its fruit."

Lent by the Ruth Bryan Strauss Memorial Foundation, N. Y. C.

PLATE XL

*82. KIDDUSH CUP   F 2118

Silver gilded, and chased.
H. 5"   D. 2½"
Augsburg, Germany, 1753-1755
Master: GS (Gottlieb Satzger)
Hallmark: R³ 256 with year letter L

Shell patterns. Inscription: "Remember the Sabbath Day to keep
it holy. Remember it with a blessing over wine."
See work of same master: Kiddush Cup F 2301, Jewish Museum,
N. Y. C.

Harry G. Friedman Collection

PLATE XLI

82   83

°83. KIDDUSH CUP WITH LID   F 3009

Silver, partly gilt, repoussé, engraved and cast.
H. (without cover) 7″   H. (with cover) 8½″   D. (lip) 2½″
Europe, 17th century
Restamping of Lemberg 1806-1807 (R³ 7989)
No mastermark. Hallmark not decipherable.

On circular chalice-foot, string ornaments with leaves and flowers. On upper part of baluster shaft, three cast volute ornaments
with rosettes, ending in animal heads. Cuppa with stylized leaf
ornaments on lower part; string ornament with flower motifs in
the upper part. Inscription around lip: the blessing of the wine.
On cover, string ornaments with leaf and flower motifs. Spherical
knop at top.

Harry G. Friedman Collection

                                                    PLATE XLI

Plate XLI   88

HABDALAH

The Sabbath (and each festival) is concluded after sunset with a ceremony called *Habdalah*, meaning "Separation," referring to the distinction of that day from ordinary weekdays. For the *Habdalah*, wine, spices and a twisted candle are used, the latter recalling ancient torchlights.

The ceremony, which is based on late antiquity custom, takes place after the conclusion of the evening meal. A container for spices (Hebrew: *b'samim*) is used, the most common of all Jewish ceremonial objects. It contains spices and aromatic plants, the use of myrtle being enjoined but not obligatory. No other ritual object shows as many variations as the spice container. The oldest pieces preserved have the well-known tower form which originated in the tower-like incense containers of the Near East. In medieval times in western countries spices were very precious and therefore kept in the tower of the city fortification, which makes it understandable that the medieval tower was reproduced for the spice containers in the European west.

Eastern European Jewry developed a special type of spice container in the form of a fruit or a flower. In parts of the Near East actual fruits are used for smelling during the *Habdalah* ceremony. In some examples the spice container is combined with the holder for the *Habdalah* light. Other combinations also occur, such as that of the cup with the spice container as its lid.

°84. SPICE CONTAINER (TOWER FORM)   JM 23-52

Silver, engraved, cutout and cast.
H. 9⅜"
Frankfort-on-the-Main, ca. 1550
Inscription: date of restoration, 1651
Portion, where mastermarks would be found, broken off

Turret, finials and flags missing. Two of the grilled windows broken. Original Gothic balustrade replaced in 1651 by present fleur-de-lys balustrade. Base flattened, and original feet (probably in lion form) lost.

Inscription (made at time balustrade was replaced): "Reha, daughter of Eleazar."

Originally in the synagogue of Friedberg, Germany. Given to the Jewish Museum of Frankfort in 1937-38. (See illustration 84a, Pl. XLII, for detail.)

Compare especially Rudolph Hallo, *Juedische Kunst aus Hessen und Nassau* (Exhibit in Marburg), Berlin 1933, No. 74, in which No. 73, Spice container of the Hessische Landes Museum, date of which can be set at 1573. See H. Frauberger; *Mitteilungen der Gesellschaft zur Erforschung Juedischer Altertuemer* I, 1900, figure 21.

PLATE XLII

84

84a

PLATE XLII

90

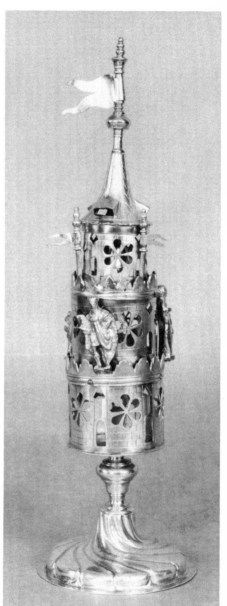

86   87

91   PLATE XLIII

85. SPICE CONTAINER   F 3440

Silver filigree, partly applied on a gilt ground with enameled flowers.
Poland, late 18th century
H. 16⅛″

Hexagonal tower for holding spices. Sides, arches over twisted columns framing vases with flowers. Pointed pediments and gilded columnettes with capitals and flags; finial, double lantern with bells and flag. Hexagonal base with bulbous shaft.

Compare: Spice Containers F 2654, F 1711; also, filigree knops of Hanukkah Menorah F 563; Jewish Museum, N. Y. C.

Harry G. Friedman Collection

*86. SPICE CONTAINER (TOWER FORM)   JM 35-52

Silver with embossed, cutout and cast ornaments.
H. 11″
Augsburg, Germany, ca. 1710-15 (R³ 216)
Master: MW (Markus or Matthias Wolff) (R³ 726)

Tower rests on male figure holding goblet. The figures of soldiers on the balustrade are 19th century additions. At top, flag (replaced).

By the same master: Torah Breastplate S 34, Cat. No. 48, Pl. XXVI; Torah Breastplate JM 30-52; Jewish Museum, N. Y. C. Pair of Torah Headpieces, Zagayski Collection, N. Y. C.; Torah Breastplate, Schwarz Collection, Tel Aviv, Israel, formerly in the Collection of Nauheim, Frankfort, Museum Juedischer Altertuemer.

Gift of the Jewish Cultural Reconstruction, Inc.

PLATE XLIII

*87. SPICE CONTAINER   F 1548

Silver, cutout, engraved, and cast.
H. 11½″
Strasbourg, Alsace-Lorraine, mid-18th century (R³ 6924)
Master: AA with dot beneath, in heart-shaped field

Three story tower, pierced rose window, roof-like spire with flag. Circular foot ornamented with twisted fluting. Figures of Moses, Aaron and David, possibly a later addition.

Gift of Henry L. Moses, N. Y. C.

PLATE XLIII

*88. SPICE CONTAINER (TURRET FORM)   J 71

Silver filigree, with semi-precious stones and enamel plaques.
H. 8⅝″
Italy, 18th century

Rectangular spice container with pyramidical roof and inverted conical base. Sides decorated with enamel plaques of biblical themes: Jacob's Dream, Moses and the Brazen Serpent, David and Bathsheba, and Susanna and the Elders.

Similar piece in Cluny Museum, Paris (catalogue of the London Exhibit of 1887). Others were in Luitpold Museum, Wuerzburg; Jewish Museum, Frankfort; Howitt Collection, London (Sale catalogue, Christie 1932).

Lent by Michael M. Zagayski, N. Y. C.

PLATE XLIV

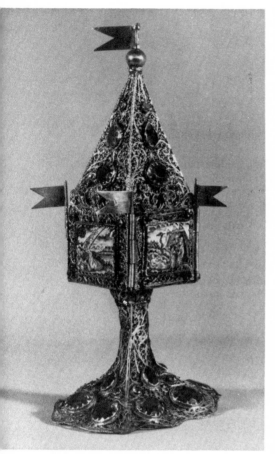

88

89

93　　　　　　　　　　　　　　Plate XLIV

*89. SPICE CONTAINER (TURRET FORM)   J 55
Silver, partly gilded; cast, engraved and openwork.
H. 10¼"
Galicia, ca. 1760-1770
Restamping of Lemberg (Lwow) 1806 (Betique 3026)
Inscription: Name of owner, Nathan Zvi Hirsch
Turret-shaped, upper part recessed, with dome and cone finial, on rectangular base. Cutout work with birds, lions and leaf decorations.
Lent by Michael M. Zagayski, N. Y. C.

PLATE XLIV

*90. SPICE CONTAINER (HEXAGONAL)   F 2496
Silver, openwork, engraved and cast.
H. 12"
Southeastern Europe, 18th century
Restamping of Brno, 1806 (R³ 9242)
Three sides show German Jewish figures in 18th-century attire, with three spice containers, two candles, and a wine cup. Above each is the appropriate blessing (abbreviated). Fourth side is decorated with flowers and animals. Above spice compartment is a gallery with signs of the zodiac. Other features are a bulbous roof, lantern with a bell, and finial with a lion holding a laver, the end of which is missing. Hexagonal base has floral decorations and supports tendrils with masks, on which rests the spice container.
Cf. Hanukkah Lamp F 2472, Cat. No. 137, Pl. LVII, and Torah Headpieces F 1988; Jewish Museum, N. Y. C.
Harry G. Friedman Collection

PLATE XLV

*91. SPICE CONTAINER   JM 34-51
Silver, pressed, cutout engraved and cast.
H. 20"
Made for the Synagogue of Berdichev 1855
Tower-shaped, surmounted by a crown, adorned with fruit and a large sunflower on top made to hold spices. Dedication inscription lists members of the congregation of Berdichev. Original red leather case, dated 1855.
Compare Torah Crowns F 268, Cat. No. 39, Jewish Museum, N. Y. C. Benguiat Collections. (See Catalogue, American Art Galleries, 1924, No. 622.)

PLATE XLV

*92. SPICE CONTAINER (PEAR-SHAPED)   F 2622
Silver, cast and pressed.
H. 10¼"
Poland (Galicia ?), ca. 1840-1850
Pear-shaped container on a vine-shaped stem decorated with flowers. Base with six rampant unicorns; between the unicorns alternating flower and fruit ornaments, also a small figure of an ox.
Harry G. Friedman Collection

PLATE XLVI

90

91

95

Plate XLV

*93. SPICE CONTAINER   F 2070

Silver, gilded, cast and hammered.
H. 4½"
Poland, 19th century
Hallmark: Right profile of man's head
Maker's Mark: NIP

Spice container in form of pear on a vine, with leaves.

Harry G. Friedman Collection

PLATE XLVI

94. SPICE CONTAINER   F 2071

Silver, gilded, cast and engraved.
H. 2½"   W. 1½"
Eastern Europe

Pear-shaped, with stem and leaves. Floral decorations.

Harry G. Friedman Collection

95. SPICE CONTAINER   M 388

Silver.
H. 9¼"
Poland, 1821
Hall or Mastermark: Stag
Weight Mark: 12

Vase holding three spice containers in the form of fruit, on long
stems, decorated with leaves and rosettes.

*96 a, b, c, d. HABDALAH CANDLESTICK WITH
DRAWER FOR SPICES   F 3661

Silver, repoussé, cast, and filigree.
H. 13"
Frankfort-on-the-Main, Germany 1710-1720
Master: Jeremias Zobel
Maker's Mark: IZ in oval (R³ 2050)
Hallmark: Frankfort-on-the-Main (R³ 2007)

Four pronged tapering holders over flat square box with drawer
for spices, set on round shaft rising from circular base with scroll
and leaf ornament. Spice box with open border and gothic gallery; four figurines, representing: (1) scribe with inkwell and
pen; (2) beadle with Torah finial and hammer (the former to
indicate his function in the synagogue, the latter to indicate his
duties to wake the congregants for the morning service by knock-
ing at their doors); (3) Matzah baker with a matzah (unleavened bread) and tool for baking matzoth; (4) slaughterer with
knife and fowl.

From the Harry G. Friedman Collection

PLATE XLVII

92

93

97   Plate XLVI

97. HABDALAH CANDLESTICK WITH DRAWER
FOR SPICES   F 346 a

Silver.
H. 9"
Augsburg (R³ 278) 1781-1783
Mastermark: Fleur-de-lys (not known)
Harry G. Friedman Collection

*98. HABDALAH CANDLESTICK WITH DRAWER
FOR SPICES   JM 36-52

Silver, hammered, with cast decoration.
H. 12¾"
Frankfort-on-the-Main, Germany, ca. 1750
Master: Roettger Herflurth
Candlestick (with movable candleholder) and spice container
(in form of a drawer), supported by a figure of a man with a
pitcher in his right hand and a cap in his left, symbolic of the
Habdalah ceremony at the close of the Sabbath (Saturday night).
By same master, Breastplate JM 33-52, Hanukkah Lamp F 2818;
Jewish Museum, N. Y. C. Other works see *Notizblatt der Gesellschaft
zur Erforschung Juedischer Kunstdenkmaeler*, 1937, No. 37, Gundersheimer und Schoenberger, *Frankfurter Hanukkah Leuchter aus Silber
und Zinn*, No. 4, p. 16-21. This piece was in the S. Nauheim Collection, Museum Juedischer Altertuemer, Frankfort-on-the-Main, Germany.
Gift of the Jewish Cultural Reconstruction, Inc.

PLATE XLVIII

*99. SPICE CONTAINER   F 2677

Silver with engraved and cast decorations.
H. 2¼"   L. 4½"   D. 2½"
Frankfort-on-the-Main, Germany, ca. 1725
Master: JDK (Johann Dabiel Kneller), 1722
Hallmark: (R³ 2058) (R³ 2007)
Unusual spice container in form of box with six partitions and
sliding cover. On top of cover, cast figure of a lion. Four baluster
feet (replacing original lion feet).
Harry G. Friedman Collection

PLATE XLVIII

*100. COMBINATION HABDALAH CUP AND
SPICE CONTAINER   S 1051

Silver, embossed cover, openwork.
H. (with cover) 7"   D. (at base) 2⅛"
Germany
Covered cup on square base in classical style. Cover designed
to serve as spice container. The inscription states that the cup
was given by Isaac Dessau and three pupils to Rabbi Nate
Ellinger (1772-1839), the teacher of Samson Raphael Hirsch,
in 1821, on his departure from the Talmud Torah of Hamburg
to become rabbi of Bingen.
Harry J. Friedman Collection

PLATE XLVIII

96a

96b

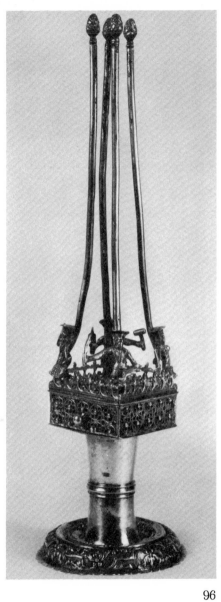

96

96c

96d

99

98

100

PLATE XLVIII

100

PASSOVER (PESAH)

Passover (Hebrew: *Pesah*) commemorates the escape of the Israelites from Egyptian bondage. The festival calls for a special service on the first two evenings of the week dedicated to it. This service is called the *Seder*, or "order," and is conducted in the home. It encompasses a festive meal and has become the most important domestic event of the Jewish year, aside from the welcoming of the Sabbath.

For the *Seder* the table is set in the most festive way. Main features are the plates and dishes containing the symbolic foods recalling the fate of the Hebrew people in Egypt and the *Pesah* meal on the eve of their liberation. Three cakes of *matzoth* (unleavened bread) are placed on a tray and covered with a cloth. They must be separated from each other which, in the seventeenth century, led to the creation of Passover plates with three tiers. Until that time simple plates were used. The Middle Ages preferred earthenware plates, and these were followed by pewter. The latter were very common until the middle of the last century, because pewter was *the* household material. During the eighteenth century, silver plates became popular with those who could afford them. The text engraved on the plates, particularly on those made of pewter, indicates the order of the ritual. There are also smaller dishes, sometimes fixed to the plate, which contain: (1) a roasted lamb bone, symbolic of the Passover sacrifice; (2) a roasted egg, referring to the festival sacrifice in the Temple; (3) a morsel of bitter herb, alluding to the bitterness which the Israelites endured in Egypt; (4) parsley or watercress which is dipped in (5) a small container of salt water, like the hyssop plant of biblical times which was dipped in the blood of the sacrificial animal; (6) the *haroseth*, a mixture of apples, raisins, and almonds mixed with cinnamon and wine; looking like mortar, intended to recall the time when the Israelites were forced to build brick walls in Egypt.

A characteristic feature of the Passover table are the wine cups of glass or silver used for the drinking of the obligatory four cups during the Passover meal. A special cup, the most precious of them all, filled with wine, stands on the table for the prophet Elijah, the forerunner of the Messianic Age.

The entire *Seder* is based upon the idea of instructing the child impressively. The text used for it is contained in the *Haggadah,* a sequence of prayers, didactic quotations, narratives taken from biblical and later texts, hymns and songs. The Haggadah book is used only in the home and not taken to the synagogue, and was therefore not subjected to the scrutiny of the rabbis. It has become the most illustrated and illuminated of all Hebrew books, *the* picture book of the Jewish home.

101. KIDDUSH CUP FOR THE PASSOVER MEAL   JM 22-52

> *Silver, repoussé and engraved decoration.*
> H. 5"
> *Fuerth, Bavaria, ca 1760-1770 (R³ 2152)*
> *Master: IR (R³ 2157)*
> Similar to Torah Headpieces JM 19-52, Cat. No. 27, Pl. XVI; Jewish Museum, N. Y. C.
> Gift of Jewish Cultural Reconstruction, Inc., from the former Jewish Museum of Frankfort-on-the-Main, Germany.

102

103

PLATE XLIX   102

104

105

106

107

PLATE LI
104

108

PLATE LII

°102. WINE CUP FOR PROPHET ELIJAH   M 395
Silver, repoussé and cast.
H. 6"   D. (at top) 2¼"   D. (at base) 2¾"
Messiah, son of David, riding on a donkey, preceded by the
prophet Elijah blowing a ram's horn; King David with harp
entering Jerusalem. Inscription on base is the blessing over wine.
                                                      PLATE XLIX

°103. WINE CUP FOR SABBATH NIGHT   M 234
Silver, partially gilded.
H. 6"   D. (at base) 3½"   D. (at top) 3¾"
Moscow, Russia, 1776
Master: ATHP
Gilded shells between vines and floral patterns. Inscription
around rim: "Elijah the Prophet, Elijah the Tishbite, Elijah of
Gilead, may he come to us speedily with the Messiah, son of
David" (from the Saturday evening service). Inscription around
base: "This cup belongs to the Holy (Burial) Society of the
Congregation of Rosenau, 1776."
                                                      PLATE XLIX

°104. PASSOVER PLATE   D 114
Faience with inscription.
D. 18"
Pesara, Italy. Date on back 1614
On rim, floral patterns and biblical scenes (Joseph revealing
himself to his brothers; the Israelites at the Passover meal in
Egypt). On separate cartouches, Moses, Aaron and David. In-
scriptions: Text of the Kiddush (Sanctification) and the order
of the Passover Eve service (Seder).
Thirteen plates of this sort are known. Place and date of origin not
definitely established.
                                                      PLATE L

°105. PASSOVER PLATE   JM 50-48
Faience, painted.
D. 9⅝"
Liverpool, England, 1788
Scalloped edge, decorated in red and moss green. On rim,
foliage and rosettes. In center, Passover scene with the Hebrew
inscription: "You shall eat in haste" (Ex. 12.11). The marked
letters indicate the year 1788.
Pewter Passover Plates F 1 and F 1390, Jewish Museum, N. Y. C.,
show the similar scenes, common in illustrated Passover haggadoth.
Gift of Stafford Lorie, London, England
                                                      PLATE L

°106. PASSOVER PLATE   F 520
Pewter.
D. 12"
Europe, 17th century
The signs of the zodiac, the Sacrifice of Isaac. Center: Adam
and Eve in Paradise (going back to Medieval haggadah illus-
trations which, as in the Serajevo Haggadah, start with the story
of the creation). Inscriptions on rim: order of Passover Eve
service. From the Petersburg Museum.
Harry G. Friedman Collection
                                                      PLATE LI

*107. PASSOVER PLATE   F 530
      Pewter.
      D. 15"
      Germany, 1771
      On rim: the order of the Passover ceremony. In center, eight-
      pointed star with Passover lamb. Between points of star: the
      four sons, the double eagle, lion, stag (alluding to the Sayings
      of the Fathers), and a flower.
      Owner inscription indicates that this plate belonged to Yehuda,
      son of Jacob, and his wife Reichle, daughter of Jacob.
      Harry G. Friedman Collection

                                                PLATE LI

*108. PASSOVER PLATE   F 2620
      Pewter with engraved decoration.
      D. 15⅛"
      Western Europe   Plate, 17th century   Engraving, 18th century
      Master: Joel Kinsburg
      Center, the four sons and paschal lamb. Also small representa-
      tions of objects on the Seder table: Kiddush cup, matzoth, etc.
      Inscription on rim: Order of the Passover Eve service. Above
      paschal lamb, maker's inscription: "Made by my hands, not to
      boast, the humble Joel Kunsburg."
      Harry G. Friedman Collection

                                                PLATE LII

*109. PASSOVER PLATE   D 115
      Brass, round.
      H. 14"   D. 15¼"
      Poland, 17th century
      Base (open work) divided into three compartments, each for
      a matzah. Upper part designed to hold various dishes for the
      Passover meal (Seder); also frames, held by lions, with inscrip-
      tion as follows: "Thus did Hillel at the time the Temple existed,"
      from the Haggadah.

                                                PLATE LIII

*110. PASSOVER PLATE   JM 84-52
      Silver with cast, cutout, and pressed decorations, with silk curtain.
      H. 18½"   D. 15"
      Vienna, Austria, 1807 (R³ 7895)
      Master: WS
      Round in shape. Interior fitted with three compartments for the
      three matzoth. Decorations: Figures of Moses, Aaron and Miriam
      and three groups of men, carrying the small dishes for the sym-
      bolic food of the Passover meal. Three trays, each to hold a
      matzah. Top ornaments: (a) Three statuettes—Moses with rod
      (part broken off), Aaron with censer, Miriam with tambourine;
      (b) six statuettes carrying on their heads dishes for seder food.
      This dish was at one time on loan to the Jewish Museum, Frankfort,
      Germany.
      Gift of Edward J. Sovatkin, N. Y. C., in memory of his mother,
      Fanny Sovatkin.

                                                PLATE LIV

109

PLATE LIII   108

110

PLATE LIV

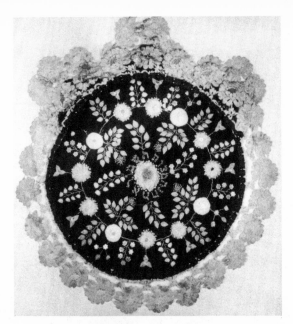

111

112

PLATE LV   110

*111. MATZOTH COVER M 53

D. 18"
Poland, 18th century

Red velvet with lace border. Rosette and leaf ornaments made
of fish scales. Three openings for the traditional matzoth, embroidered with the designations, "Kohen," "Levi," and "Israel."

PLATE LV

*112. OMER CALENDAR IN FORM OF TORAH ARK F 3411

*Parchment manuscript with painted decorations in color, in
wooden case.*
H. (scroll) 8½" H. (with top piece) 16"
H. (Case) 10½" x 10½"
Holland, 18th century

Case in shape of Torah Ark. Door, a frame for Ten Commandments on parchment. On back of door, parchment with Omer
benediction for days from Pesah (Passover) to Shabuoth.
(Roman numerals have been put over the Hebrew letters.) On
parchment with Ten Commandments is the inscription: "And
the Lord had blessed Abraham in all things" (Gen. 24.1). Dotting on Hebrew letters of this verse indicates date 1763 (?).

Manuscript decorated with elaborate painted floral patterns.

Omer Scroll is used in the synagogue for counting of the 49 days (7
weeks) between the 2nd day of Passover and Shabuoth—Lev. 23.15,
16: "And ye shall count unto you from the morrow after the day
of rest, from the day that ye brought the sheaf of the waving; seven
weeks shall there be complete; even unto the morrow after the seventh
week shall ye number fifty days."

Harry G. Friedman Collection

PLATE LV

*113. KIDDUSH CUP (FOR FESTIVALS) F 32

Silver, gilded.
H. 4⅛" D. (rim) 3" D. (base) 2⅓"
Frankfort-on-the-Main, Germany, 1737
Master: JPB (Johann Peter Beyer)
Hallmark: R³ 2005

Circular base with vertical ribs; cup rising in slender flower-like
form. Three cartouches with inscriptions. Above, floral ornamentation with rampant lions.

Inscriptions: Around rim, "And Moses declared the set feasts
of the Lord unto the children of Israel" (Lev. 23.44). On cartouches: "For seven days shall ye eat unleavened bread" (Lev.
23.6); "Seven weeks shall ye count for thyself" (Lev. 23.15);
"And ye shall dwell in booths seven days" (Lev. 23.42).

Other works by the same master include Hanukkah lamps; cf. Gundersheimer aud Schoenberger, *Notizblatt der Gesellschaft zur Erforschung
Juedischer Altertuemer*, vol. 34, 1937, No. 2, p. 13.

Harry G. Friedman Collection

PLATE LVI

*114. KIDDUSH CUP (from frankfort synagogue)   F 3000

Gold.
H. 5-1/16"
Frankfort-on-the-Main, Germany, ca. 1600

Vases with flowers alternating with cartouches on which are lion, stag and unicorn.

Inscriptions in cartouches: (a) Around lion, "Three times in the year all thy males shall appear before the Lord God" (Ex. 23.17). The date 1650 is indicated by marked letters. (b) Around the unicorn, "Repaired during presidency of Raphael, son of Paer (Baer) Hahn Segal (Levite)." Substantially the same inscription is repeated above the foot, with the date 1769. (c) On lip, "Observe the Sabbath to keep it holy" (Deut. 5.12).

"Remembering that the Lord God is the Creator and Preserver of the world. Over the good wine let Him be remembered and over the golden vessel let His praise be heard . . . T (abbreviation of name) had this cup restored at his expense in the year 1707." The date is indicated by marked letters in the words, "May He restore in joy His abode." The repairs of 1769 referred to in the inscription may have changed an original high foot to the low 18th century cast base.

The cup was formerly in the Jewish Museum of Frankfort from where it was taken by the Gestapo. It was recovered by the Jewish Cultural Reconstruction, Inc. and given to The Jewish Museum, N. Y. C., in 1951.

PLATE LVI

115. KIDDUSH CUP FOR FESTIVALS   F 217

Silver with engraved decoration, inside gilded.
H. 4½"   D. (lip) 2½"
London, England, 1799-1800
Hallmark: R³ 7140, Yearletter C, R³ 7203
Master: IW

Decorations indicating the festivals: Rosh Hashanah (New Year), two men blowing the shofar; Sukkoth (tabernacles), man holding lulab (palm branch) and ethrog (citron); Pesah Seder (Passover meal), Passover Eve scene showing figures standing around table with Paschal Lamb as prescribed in Exodus 12.11; Shabuoth, Moses with the Tablets of the Law.

Inscriptions: "And Moses declared the set feasts of the Lord unto the Children of Israel." (Lev. 23.44)

Harry G. Friedman Collection

113

114

PLATE LVI

HIGH HOLIDAYS

The days beginning with *Rosh Hashanah* and ending with *Yom Kippur* are called the "Ten Days of Penitence." The basic idea attached to *Rosh Hashanah* (New Year) is that of God being the judge over every individual. This idea produced a special liturgy and many customs of which one of the most significant is the blowing of the *Shofar*, a horn which in ancient times was mainly an instrument for signals in war and peace. Its sounding on *Rosh Hashanah* has found manifold interpretations. They can be summed up as a call to repentance and to spiritual regeneration.

The *Shofar* is made from the horn of an animal of the sheep or goat family, usually the horn of a ram. It is put into extremely hot water so that it may become flexible enough to be shaped in the traditional slightly flattened and sharply curved manner. It is forbidden to decorate the *Shofar* with painting or to cover its mouthpiece with metal. The only ornament permitted is carving, and this is found particularly on older examples. For the carving, the biblical text referring to the sounding of the *Shofar* is used. In some cases the donor's name appears, or the location of the congregation in which the *Shofar* was used.

The *Shofar* is also sounded once in a long tone at the conclusion of *Yom Kippur,* the Day of Atonement, signalizing the ending of the day of fasting. The main use of the *Shofar* in the synagogue takes place on the New Year. In Israel today the *Shofar* is used for public announcements and regularly blown before the Sabbath commences.

°116. ROSH HASHANAH PLATE   F 2978

Faience, with blue and white decorations, and inscription in black.
D. 9½″
Delft, Holland, ca. 1700
Maker's Mark: RAK

Special dishes used in the home on the evening of the New Year for serving an apple dipped in honey, with the blessing: "Renew unto us a happy and sweet year." Inscription: "Rosh Hashanah" (New Year).

Gift of Theresa Goel

PLATE LVII

°117. RAM'S HORN   JM 2-49

Horn with engraved inscription.
L. 15″
Germany, 1781-82

Inscription: Front, "I, the humble Joseph son of Wolf of the city of Dieburg . . ." (Hesse). Back, "Blow the great trumpet."
PLATE LVIII

רֹאשׁ וּשָׁנָה

116

PLATE LVII

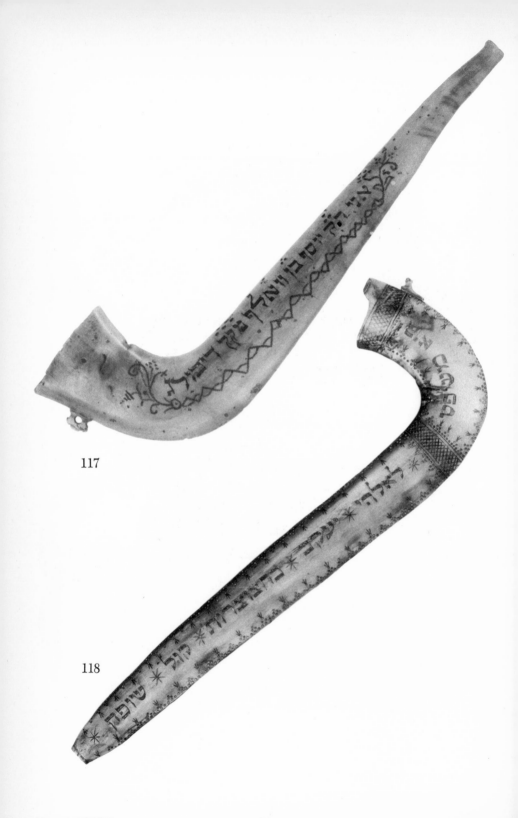

117

118

Plate LVIII   116

120

121

117   PLATE LIX

*118. RAM'S HORN   F 502

   Horn with engraved inscription.
   L. 17"
   Europe, 18th century

   Inscription: "Blow the horn at the new moon, At the full moon
   on our feast-day. For it is a statute for Israel, An ordinance of
   the God of Jacob" (Ps. 81.45). "With trumpets and the sound
   of the horn" (Ps. 98.6).

   Harry G. Friedman Collection

                                                   PLATE LVIII

119. SHOFAR AND CASE   F 2832

   Ram's horn, with case of brown leather.
   L. (Shofar) 16⅛"   L. (Case) 17"
   Germany, ca. 1800

   Inscriptions on case: "Wolf, son of N (perhaps Nathan) . . .
   from Hilberstadt . . ." Also, "With trumpets and sound of the
   horn shout ye before the King, the Lord" (Ps. 98.6).

   Harry G. Friedman Collection

*120. BELT BUCKLE FOR THE DAY OF ATONEMENT F 3482

   Silver.
   H. 2½"   L. 4½"
   Poland, 19th century

   Cartouche between eagles. Inscription from the prayers for the
   Day of Atonement: "For on this day shall atonement be made
   for you, to cleanse you: from all your sins before the Lord shall
   ye be clean" (Lev. 16.30).

   On the High Holidays traditional garb is customary—the so-called
   kittel, or loose garment of white linen, held together at the waist
   by a belt.

   Harry G. Friedman Collection

                                                      PLATE LIX

*121. BELT BUCKLE FOR THE DAY OF ATONEMENT F 3194

   Silver, repoussé work.
   H. 2½"   L. 4¾"
   Lemberg (Lwow), 1863
   Master: TR   Hallmark: R³ 7988
   Similar to Belt Buckle F 3482, Cat. No. 120, Pl. LIX, Jewish Mu-
   seum, N. Y. C.
   Harry G. Friedman Collection

                                                      PLATE LIX

SUKKOTH

Sukkoth (Feast of Tabernacles), a seven day period, celebrates the coming of autumn, the late harvest, and commemorates the divine protection enjoyed by Israel during its wanderings in the wilderness. It is the festival of thanksgiving. Jews eat their meals in a Sukkah, or booth, erected in the open air and so covered with branches that the stars can be seen through the roof. Roof and wall may be richly adorned with fruit and vegetables.

During the recital of special hymns in the morning synagogue service for *Sukkoth*, the *Lulab*, palm leaf cluster to which myrtle and willow branches are attached, and the *Ethrog* (citron) are taken in hand and, at prescribed points, moved in all directions. The *Ethrog*, when not in use, remains in a special box for its protection. The box has assumed in its outer shape the form of the fruit itself. Other shapes of the *Ethrog* box can also be found. These boxes are the only significant ritualistic object created for the Sukkoth festival. There are no specimens of *Ethrog* box preserved which antedate the eighteenth century.

122

°122. CONTAINER FOR CITRON F 2897

> *Silver with hammered and embossed decoration.*
> L. 5″   L. (with stem) 6½″
> *Holland, 1889*
> *Master: CIB (R³ 7545) (R³ 7542 with M)*

In center, the initials of the owner "JF" surrounded by scrolled border.

Harry G. Friedman Collection

PLATE LX

HANUKKAH

Hanukkah, the Feast of Dedication, is celebrated for eight days. Josephus refers to it as the Festival of Light. It commemorates the rededication of the Temple in Jerusalem after the victory of Judah Maccabee over the Syrians in 165 B.C.E. The eight days are explained by the tale of the miraculous cruse of oil which burned in the Temple seven days longer than its actual measure which was meant for one day only. The main characteristic of the festival is the kindling of lights, one on the first night, two on the second night, adding one more on each succeeding night. No practical use can be made of the eight lights because they are holy. As light was a precious commodity in days gone by, it became customary to add a ninth light which made the use of the others permissible. This ninth light became the *Shammash,* or servant light, which assumed the task of kindling the other lights on Hanukkah.

The Hanukkah lamps developed from a simple Roman oil lamp made of clay into the elaborate creations of later times. Two definite types can be distinguished. One, which can be called the bench type, shows clearly that Hanukkah was originally celebrated in the home only. It is typically rather small and has a back wall for safety reasons. This back wall gave the artist an opportunity to add meaningful ornaments as well as texts.

When, in the course of the centuries, it became necessary to kindle the Hanukkah lights in the synagogue for those wayfarers who spent nights in the adjacent quarters, the bench type could not be enlarged advantageously. The designers therefore went back to the shape of the Menorah in the Temple, preserved not only in the biblical description but also in numerous manuscript illustrations. Two lights were added to it, and the *Menorah* type of Hanukkah lamp was created. This development took place during the Middle Ages. We know that in the fifteenth century the Menorah type was common. In the synagogue, the Hanukkah Menorah was placed to the right of the Torah Ark (south) all year round, corresponding to the location of the golden Menorah in the Temple of old.

From the Menorah type of the Hanukkah lamp in the synagogue, the smaller Hanukkah Menorah for the Jewish home was developed. This shape was particularly well suited to the use of candles, which have become increasingly popular since the eighteenth century.

°123. HANUKKAH LAMP (FOR OIL)   F 2125

> *Brass, cast.*
> *H. 12¾″ W. 15½″*
> *Italy, 17th century*
>
> Balustrade with platform for missing glass oil-containers. Back wall with four columns carrying a molding and three arches. Central lunette has holder for missing servant-light oil-container.
>
> Compare: M. Narkiss, "Hanukkah Lamps," No. 134; also "The Hanukkah Lamp," in *Israelitisches Familienblatt,* Hamburg, Germany, No. 7, 1929, p. 53.
>
> Harry G. Friedman Collection
>
>   PLATE LXI

123

124

121   Plate LXI

125

126

PLATE LXII 122

128

129

PLATE LXIII

130

131

PLATE LXIV   124

*124. HANUKKAH LAMP   L 14-54
Brass, cast.
H. 5½″   W. 6¾″
Italy, 14th century
Back wall is triangular in shape. Decorations in relief, on car-
touches, are (a) two lions, (b) dragon. Below this ornamen-
tation is (c) inscription from Prov. 6.23, "For the commandment
is a lamp, and the law is light." Under the inscription is (d)
colonnade with intersecting arches. From base of the back wall
project eight oil burners and at the left the servant light.
Cf. Sammlung Dr. Albert Figdor, Wien, vol. 5, p. 465; *Mitteilung
der Gesellschaft zur Erforschung Juedischer Kunstdenkmaeler*, vol.
III-IV, October 1903, pp. 45-49.
Lent by Judge Irving Lehman Collection, Temple Emanu-El,
N. Y. C. (From the Figdor Collection)

                                                   PLATE LXI

*125. HANUKKAH LAMP   F 129
Brass, cast.
H. 7¼″   W. 8¾″
Italy, ca. 1600
Servant light missing. Italian Renaissance motifs: Two angels
blowing trumpets, vases, and lion to which the missing servant
light was attached. Motif of center leg may be an insignia of
the family which owned the lamp. At top, figure of Judith with
sword and the head of Holofernes. Beneath his figure, inscription: "Judith."
Harry G. Friedman Collection

                                                   PLATE LXII

*126. HANUKKAH LAMP   F 3084
Brass, cast.
H. 7⅜″   W. 8-3/16″
Italy, form of ca. 1600; cast later
Decoration: Fountain flanked by two lions. Eight oil burners.
Servant light missing.
Harry G. Friedman Collection

                                                   PLATE LXII

127. HANUKKAH LAMP (FOR OIL)   F 3692
Silver.
H. 11″   W. 9¼″
Holland, mid-18th century
Control Stamp of The Hague
Typical rocaille form of backwall and floral decorations around
large center cartouche for inscription. Three flowers in high re-
lief connect backwall with oil burners. No trace of attachment
for servant light.
Harry G. Friedman Collection

*128. HANUKKAH LAMP   L 18-54
Silver, partly gilded, repoussé ornament and cast figures.
H. 10″   W. 11¼″
Frankfort-on-the-Main, Germany, ca. 1680
Hallmark: R³ 2004
Master: SV or VS (S in V), perhaps Valentin Schueler

Figures: Lion of Judah, Judith and her maid; a woman; a man with a trumpet; stags; pelicans; and one-headed eagle. See piece by same master: Sabbath Lamp F 2707, Cat. No. 70, Pl. XXXIV, Jewish Museum, N. Y. C.; Hanukkah Menorah, Hist. Museum, Frankfort-on-the-Main. See Gundersheimer and Schoenberger, "Frankfurter Hanukah-Leuchter aus Silber und Zinn," 1937, No. 8. Lent by Collection of Michael M. Zagayski, N. Y. C.

PLATE LXIII

°129. HANUKKAH LAMP   JM 27-53
Silver, partly gilded, cast, engraved and embossed; for oil decorations.
H. 11¾″ W. 12″
Western Europe, ca. 1700
Center, Hanukkah Menorah, between Moses and Aaron; right, figure of Judith and of Judah Maccabee; left, figure of a woman and a trumpeter holding the servant light; at sides, lions, bears, acanthus leaves and fruit ornaments. Inscriptions: Right: The blessings over the Hanukkah lights; left, the prayer after the kindling of the lights; top, coat of arms showing an arm holding a rosette-ornament; encircled by Latin inscription: *Providentia tutamur*—"We are protected by Providence."
For similar lamp see "Rheinischer Verein fuer Denkmalpflege und Heimatschuetz," 1931, 1, *Aus der Geschichte der Juden im Rheinland.* Elizabeth Moses; *Juedische Kult-und Kunstdenkmaeler in den Rheinlaendern*, p. 161.
Gift of Samuel Lemberg, N. Y.

PLATE LXIII

°130. HANUKKAH LAMP   F 197
Silver; repoussé and cast work.
H. 13½″ W. 11¾″
Nuremberg, Germany, 1710-1720 (R³ 3767)
Master: MS in oval field
Shell finial. Seven-branched candlestick over a frame, revealing parchment bearing the Hanukkah benediction for the kindling of the lights, and other benedictions and prayers, including the hymn *Rock of Ages*. Below are eight oil burners with figure of a knight to represent Judah Maccabee on the left, and figure of Judith with the head of Holofernes on the right. Servant light on left. Oil pitcher missing.
Harry G. Friedman Collection

PLATE LXIV

°131. HANUKKAH LAMP (FOR OIL)   F 948
Silver, repoussé and openwork.
H. 6½″ W. 7½″
Frankfort-on-the-Main, Germany, late 18th century (R³ 2016)
Master: Johann Christian Hetzel (1793)
Embossed decoration: Nine-branched Menorah in a cartouche, held by confronted rampant lions; over cartouche crown. Rectangular covered box with oil burners set on small cast lions. Servant light, rectangular oil-container with flag.
Good example of the Frankfort type. Cf. *Notizblatt der Gesellschaft zur Erforschung Juedischer Kunstdenkmaeler*, No. 34, 1937, No. 5.
Harry G. Friedman Collection

PLATE LXIV

132

133

 PLATE LXV

134

135

PLATE LXVI   128

136

137

PLATE LXVII

*132. HANUKKAH LAMP (FOR OIL)   F 2837
Brass, hammered and cutout; with sides.
H. 11⅛″   W. 9½″
Holland, 18th century
Vase surrounded by flower patterns; sides also have floral motifs.
Harry G. Friedman Collection
                                        PLATE LXV
*133. HANUKKAH LAMP   JM 13-47
Brass, cast and cutout; silver-plated cartouche.
H. 8½″   W. 11⅛″   W. (with basin for oil drippings) 12½″
Holland, inscription date 1757
Servant light and side pieces missing. Inscription on cartouche:
"And They shall light the lamps thereof to give light over against
it" (Ex. 25.37); and "A memorial to Isaac Israel Baron (or
Bravo) who consecrated [this lamp] to the holy congregation
in the year 1757."
In 1850 the lamp was brought from Jamaica. Its previous history is
not known.
                                        PLATE LXV
*134. HANUKKAH LAMP   F 2116
Pewter.
H. 8¾″   H. (with accessories) 11″   W. 8¾″
Frankfort-on-the-Main, Germany, late 18th century
Master's Mark: IPH (Johann Philip Henschel) above rosette
Cutout and engraved design on back wall. Row of eight oil
burners on bench, dripping pan. Base with ball feet. Small oil
pitcher (reminder of the miraculous cruse of oil) to the left,
servant light to the right.
Harry G. Friedman Collection
                                        PLATE LXVI
*135. HANUKKAH LAMP (FOR OIL)   F 2370
Pewter, cast and engraved.
H. 9⅜″   W. 9″
Horb-on-the-Neckar, Germany, 18th century
Master: Carl Sichler
Cherubim on the sides, shell finial, and central floral ornament.
Hebrew lettering. Missing are the oil jar to the left and two
little buckets for dripping oil.
The Bezalel Museum Palestine (Narkiss, No. 141) has a similar lamp.
The Nauheim Collection, Frankfort, Germany, had one made by
Johann Carl, the son of Carl Sichler. (See: *Die Sammlung Nauheim,*
1937.) The Jewish Museum, N. Y. C., has two 19th century Hanukkah
lamps of this type, F 105 by Master 1DR, and F 1839 by Master GK.
Harry G. Friedman Collection
                                        PLATE LXVI
*136. HANUKKAH LAMP WITH TWO SABBATH
CANDLE HOLDERS   F 3032
Brass, cast, with cutout work.
H. 13″   W. 12″
Poland, 18th century
Back wall of lamp in form of building front, perhaps intended
to depict a synagogue facade. Sides: Stylized lions with Sabbath
candleholders; bird ornaments on top and sides.
Cf. Hanukkah lamps, F 2799, F 2664, and F 2486, Jewish Museum,
N. Y. C. Also see M. Narkiss, *The Hanukkah Lamp,* Jerusalem, 1939;
No. 88.
Harry G. Friedman Collection
                                        PLATE LXVII

*137. HANUKKAH LAMP (FOR OIL)   F 2472
Silver, repoussé and cast.
H. 11"   W.   11½"
Eastern Europe, early 18th century
Master: BK
Hanukkah Menorah with side panels. Back wall ornamented
with Menorah and crown. Eight oil burners flanked by two
figures, one holding the servant light and the other an oil jar;
both figures are attired in typical garb of Jews of first half of
18th century. Floral and bird decorations.
Compare Spice Container F 2496, Cat. No. 90, Pl. XLV, Jewish
Museum, N. Y. C.
Harry G. Friedman Collection
                                                PLATE LXVII
*138. HANUKKAH LAMP   S 260
Silver, partly gilded, repoussé and cast openwork.
H. 28½"   W. 17½"
Brody (Galicia) 1787 (L. Lepszy, p. 67)
Master: B
       ZK
Torah Ark surmounted by crown held by two griffons; on either
side of the Torah Ark are two columns and scroll work, topped
with vases of flowers. Top ornament: Birds, and columns on
either side. Below the Torah Ark, row of eight oil burners in
form of lions. Lower ornamentation: Double-headed eagle in
cartouche, between two dolphins.
Same group, M. Narkiss, *The Hanukkah Lamp,* published Jerusalem,
1939; Hanukkah Lamp No. 118, Boston University; Hanukkah Lamp
No. 98, London Jewish Museum. Copy of same type, F 1834, Jewish
Museum, N. Y. C., recently made in Cuzgo, Peru, shape resembling
that of a wooden Polish Torah Ark.
                                                PLATE LXVIII
 139. HANUKKAH LAMP   F 102
Silver filigree with cast ornaments.
H. 12"   W. 11¾"
Southern Poland or Ukraine, early 19th century
Weight mark: 12
Maker's Mark: Running quadruped
Standing lamp. Eight small pitchers placed on a bench serve
as oil burners. A double door in center, modeled after a Torah
Ark, is flanked by two columns on which are flowers. Over the
Torah Ark is a double-headed eagle, above which are the Tablets
of the Law surmounted by an elaborate crown with a finial in
the form of a bird with a bell in its beak. On left side is a candle-
holder, on right an oil pitcher, evidently not original.
See: Hanukkah Lamp F 94, Jewish Museum, N. Y. C.
Harry G. Friedman Collection
*140. HANUKKAH LAMP   F 3401
Pewter, cast, with engraved decorations.
H. 8"   W. 9¼"
Hanau, Germany
Master: ECB with swan
Bench with oil burners along back wall. Left, snuffer; right,
servant light. Originally lions held these objects, but the corners
have been cut. Center, figure of man (Aaron?) kindling the
Seven-Branched Candlestick. Inscription, initials of the owner.
Harry G. Friedman Collection
                                                PLATE LXIX

138

Plate LXVIII   132

140

141

133   Plate LXIX

°141. HANUKKAH MENORAH   F 3017

Silver.
H. 16″   W. 12¼″
Hamburg, Germany, 17th century
Master: C
*   I B*

Shaft (on tripod base) with figure of Judah Maccabee as finial. Simple arms with square oil burners.

Harry G. Friedman Collection

PLATE LXIX

°142. HANUKKAH LAMP   S 563

Silver.
H. 17″   W. 14½″
Frankfort-on-the-Main, Germany, early 18th century
Master: IAB (Johann Adam Boller) R³ 2054

Eight branches and servant light with oil burners. Central, tapered shaft with calices rising from small, round platform with gallery and ending in similar gallery. On top: Figurine of Judith with the head of Holofernes in the left hand; the raised right hand originally held a sword.

On octagonal base four enamel medallions, red on white with scenes from Genesis: (1) Rebecca at the well (ch. 24); (2) Jacob's dream (ch. 28); (3) Jacob rolling the stone from the well (ch. 29); (4) Jacob wrestling with the angel (ch. 32). The eight arms with alternating knops and filigree buds.

This Menorah belonged to Jacob H. Schiff and was given to The Jewish Museum by his daughter, Mrs. Felix M. Warburg.

PLATE LXX

°143. HANUKKAH MENORAH   L 11-54

Silver, gilt.
H. 14¾″   W. 11½″
Naumburg, Germany, 1701

Fine early example of Menorah for use with candles for the home. Base and shaft similar to ordinary candleholders.

Lent by Mr. and Mrs. Siegfried Bendheim, N. Y. C.

PLATE LXXI

°144. HANUKKAH MENORAH FOR SYNAGOGUE   F 2831

Brass, cast.
H. 44″   W.   44″
Austria, ca. 1800

Baluster shaft with floral finial; eight lights; also extra arm (servant light) in front.

Harry G. Friedman Collection

PLATE LXXI

142

PLATE LXX

143

144

°145. HANUKKAH MENORAH FOR SYNAGOGUE   F 3034

Brass, cast.
H. 51¼″ W. 33½″
Poland, ca. 1700

Baluster shaft on round base supported by three lions. Decorated with leaves and flowers. Elaborate arms for eight candleholders. Figure 8-shaped parts with bird heads, separated by six knops.

The two inner arms on either side of the shaft are joined. Bird with outstretched wings on top.

Harry G. Friedman Collection

PLATE LXXII

146

°146. HANUKKAH MENORAH FOR SYNAGOGUE   F 2658

Brass.
H. 44″   W. 46″
Eastern Europe, 18th century

Right, S-curve arms fitted into hand-shaped sockets; also servant light (shammash) in front.

Harry G. Friedman Collection

PLATE LXXIII

146a. HANUKKAH MENORAH FOR SYNAGOGUE   F 195

Brass, cast.
H. 22″   W. 29″
Germany, 18th century

Baluster shaft and branch-like arms. Distinguished by its servant light, a man with flat hat, which used to be worn on festive occasion. (Nose is chipped off.)

Harry G. Friedman Collection

PLATE LXXIII   138

PURIM

Purim, the Feast of Lots, commemorates the escape of the Jews from destruction, as related in the Book of Esther. It is the dramatic story of Hadassah—Esther—who became Queen of Persia. At the risk of her life, she managed to save her people after learning from her relative, Mordecai, of the treachery of Haman, a courtier who out of personal vengeance tried to exterminate all the Jews in the Persian empire. This story is read in the synagogue from a parchment scroll *(Megillath Esther)* in a traditional chant. The *Megillah* has only one roller, as distinct from the Torah with its two rollers. It is customary to interrupt the reading of the *Megillah* with noisemaking every time the name of the villain, Haman, is mentioned in the text, as if to obliterate it.

In the Book of Esther the word for God does not occur. The artists could therefore feel at greater liberty to illustrate and decorate it, thereby making it the only biblical book in Judaism in which the text is traditionally accompanied by pictures—but, curiously enough, only when it has the form of a scroll.

The *Megillah* was usually placed in a container, frequently made of silver, to protect the scroll. These containers became a popular gift from a bride to a bridegroom. This accounts for their rather frequent incidence.

Purim is also dedicated to remembering the poor and presenting gifts to friends *(Shalah Manoth).* For these gifts special plates are used, often made of pewter. Usually quotations from the Book of Esther are put on the plates, in addition to scenes from the narrative. The triumph of Mordecai is the most popular scene in the illustrations.

---

*147. SCROLL OF ESTHER   F 2522

> *Manuscript on parchment in wooden cylindrical case, with silver trim and coral finial.*
> *H. (scroll) 11½″   H. (rollers) 18½″*
> *Italy, early 18th century*

Cartouche on case inscribed "Isaac di Modona."

Harry G. Friedman Collection

PLATE LXXIV

---

*148. SCROLL OF ESTHER   M 81

> *Manuscript on parchment in cylindrical gilded silver case.*
> *H. (scroll) 4⅛″   H. (roller) 8¼″*
> *Galicia, ca. 1750-1760*
> *Restamping of Lemberg 1806-1807 (R³ 7989)*

Decorated with scenes from the story of Esther: Esther being presented to the King; Haman leading Mordecai through the streets of Susa, Haman's wife Seresh in the background; Haman and his sons on the gallows. Bird finial on dome-like top. Monkey on pull-tab.

PLATE LXXIV

147

148

PLATE LXXIV   140

149

149a

PLATE LXXV

*149-149a. SCROLL OF ESTHER   D 76 and D 79
Parchment with engraved text in engraved brass case.
H. 10⅛"   D. 2"
Case: Near East, 19th century
Scroll: Italy, mid-17th century
Case: Cylindrical in shape with engraved floral decorations.
Removable lid at top of case, surmounted by crown finial. In-
scription around center of case indicates that it contains an
Esther Scroll.
Scroll: Ornamented with engraved illustrations framed in arched
portals. In niches, under decorative masks, King, Queen and
courtiers on socles decorated with nineteen scenes from the
Book of Esther. Above portals, broken pediments with lions and
finials of vases and flowers. Below pediments, between caryat-
ides, four city-street scenes, repeated five times. Between pediments, flower vases with masks and birds. At beginning of scroll,
blank shield (no inscription), surrounded by masks, peacocks
and parrots. At left, large vase with flowers and hovering but-
terfly and insects, vase itself decorated with birds and mask.
Monkey to left of vase, squirrel to right. Inscription on vase
rim, "By Salomone D'Italia."

                                                PLATE LXXV

*150. SCROLL OF ESTHER   JM 70-48
Silver case with handle, cast, gilded filigree, with semi-precious
stones.
H. (scroll) 2½"   H. (roller) 7½"
Eastern Europe, late 18th century
Fine example of elaborate design.
Gift of Louis M. Rabinowitz, Brooklyn, N. Y.

                                                PLATE LXXVI

*151. PURIM PLATE   F 2776
Pewter with engraved decorations.
D. 9½"
Germany (?) 1775
Decorations: Engraving of Mordecai on horseback. Inscription
on rim: "Sending portions one to another and gifts to the poor"
(Esther 9.22).
Harry G. Friedman Collection

                                                PLATE LXXVI

*152. PURIM PLATE   F 769
Pewter with engraved decorations.
D. 9⅜"
Probably Holland, ca. 1700
Engraving: Germany, 1768
Master: Jan Hidd . . . (rest of the name indecipherable)
In center: Haman leading Mordecai on horseback.
Date 1768. Inscription on rim: ". . . sending portions to one
another, and gifts to the poor" (Esther 9.22). Other inscription:
"This plate belongs to Sussman ben Mordecai Lengsfelder and
his wife."
Harry G. Friedman Collection

                                                PLATE LXXVI

151

150

152

PLATE LXXVI

CIRCUMCISION

According to biblical precept, the son of Jewish parents has to be circumcised on the eighth day of his life, except when reasons of health call for postponement. The person officiating *(Mohel)* proclaims the importance of his office by having his instruments and the cases for them richly ornamented. The handle of the knife, particularly, has developed into an artistic object.

154

153. CIRCUMCISION KNIFE   J 46
Handle of silver with cut decorations; double-edged blade.
L. (handle) 3⅝″   L. (total) 8¼″
Europe, 16th century

On handle: Benediction, circumcision scene, animal and floral ornamentation.

Lent by Michael M. Zagayski, N. Y. C.

°154. CIRCUMCISION KNIFE   F 2206
Silver, partly gilt, amber handle, garnets and baroque pearls.
L. 7½″
Western Europe, possibly Germany, ca. 1720

Harry G. Friedman Collection

PLATE LXXVII

°155. FLASK FOR CIRCUMCISION   F 3638
Silver.
H. 4″   W. 2¼″
Central Europe, 17th century

Circumcision scene, engraved on two sides. Inscription: "Joseph Utz" (owner). (See illustration 155a for another view.)

Harry G. Friedman Collection

PLATE LXXVIII

PLATE LXXVII   144

155

155a

145   PLATE LXXVIII

156

°156. CIRCUMCISION PLATE   M 249

Silver.
L. 14¼″   W. 10¼″
Poland, 18th century
Hall mark: E. Beuque 1555

Oval shape. In center, the Sacrifice of Isaac. On rim, the signs
of the zodiac, with sign of the Ram placed directly above the
ram in the biblical scene. With the Crown of Priesthood on
his head, Abraham is depicted as a priest offering a sacrifice.

Inscription from Gen. 22.3ff, tells of Abraham taking his son to
Mount Moriah for sacrifice.

PLATE LXXIX

PLATE LXXIX   146

157

Red velvet, embroidered.
H. 28½″   W. 26½″
Germany, 1749

Scene depicting circumcision ceremony, above inscription. Circular border, also containing inscription. Vines and floral motifs in four corners.

Inscriptions: Border. "And Abraham circumcised his son, Isaac, after eight days as God commanded him" (Gen. 21.4). Center: "This is the chair of Elijah . . . (date unclear; probably 1768) . . . presented in memory of Issachar Baer and his wife."

Cf. H. Frauberger, "Ueber alte Kultusgegenstaende in Synagoge und Haus," *Mitteilungen der Gesellschaft zur Erforschung Juedischer Kunstdenkmaeler;* Frankfort, 1903, vol. 3-4, p. 90.

Gift of Dr. S. A. Buchenholz

PLATE LXXX

AMULETS

The Amulet *(Kame'ah)* worn for purposes of protection against misfortune, particularly sickness and the "evil eye," consists of a piece of parchment with "magic" texts placed inside a metal container. It can also be worn as an ornament, usually of silver, with the word *Shaddai* (the Almighty) engraved on it. While amulets were rather popular, particularly among the Jewish population of the Mediterranean countries and the Near East, they have repeatedly been denounced by some rabbinical authorities and their use condemned as superstition.

°158. AMULET   F 2101

> *Silver filigree.*
> *H. 5″ W. 3¾″*
> *Italy, ca. 1900*

Inscription: "Shaddai" (Almighty) in center.

Harry G. Friedman Collection

PLATE LXXXI

°159. AMULET   JM 16-21

> *Silver.*
> *H. 5″ W. 2½″*
> *Rome, Italy, 17th century*
> *Hallmark type: R³ 7433*
> *Master: VE or VF*

Book in arch between two lions. Beneath, the Sacrifice of Isaac. Compare J 208, Michael M. Zagayski Collection, N. Y. C.

PLATE LXXXI

°160. AMULET   F 2097

> *Silver, cast, partially gilded, with cutout decoration.*
> *H. 5½″ W. 4″*
> *Italy, ca. 1800*

Center panel opening for insertion of manuscript; the word "Shaddai" (Almighty) on the back of the manuscript shows through the opening. Decorations: The Priestly Crown, Tablets of the Law, censer, and the Seven-Branched Candlestick.

Harry G. Friedman Collection

PLATE LXXXI

158

160

159

149

PLATE LXXXI

TEFILLIN

According to the command "they (the fundamental doctrines of Judaism) shall be for a sign on thy hands and as frontlets between thine eyes" (Deut. 6.8). At the time of morning prayer, *Tefillin* (Phylacteries) are worn. They are small cubes containing the following passages from the Pentateuch, written on parchment: Ex. 13.1-10; Ex. 13.11-16; Deut. 6.4-9; Deut. 11.13-21. They are bound with leather bands on the left arm and on the forehead between the eyes. On exhibit here are cases for the Tefillin, made for their protection, usually of silver. The cubic form of the *Tefillin* distinguished them from amulets, which were usually round.

°161. TEFILLIN CASES   M 248

Silver, engraved.
H. 2¼″   W. 2½″   D. 3¼″
Warsaw, Poland, 19th century
Master: I. Rosenzweig

With engraved decoration. Case for the phylactery for the hand: floral design on top; the four sides engraved with text and the animals mentioned in the Sayings of the Fathers: "Be strong as a leopard, light as an eagle, fleet as a hart, and strong as a lion to do the will of thy Father who is in heaven" (5.23). Case for the phylactery for the head. Inscription: "O my dove, that art in the clefts of the rock" (Song of Songs 2.14). On opposite side three sheep under tree, with text: "Israel is a scattered sheep" (Jer. 50.17). On top name of owner Jacob Brodsky.

See George Loukomski, *Jewish Art in European Synagogues*, London, England, 1947, p. 176.

Mintz Collection

                                                    PLATE LXXXII

°162. CASES FOR PHYLACTERIES   JM 69-48

Silver, gilded, appliqué, filigree and cast.
H. 2⅛″   Base: 3⅜″ x 2⅜″
Poland, late 18th century

Two confronted, crowned, rampant lions, holding a square frame over which is a crown. In the frame is abbreviation indicating one is for the arm, the other for the head. The appliqué decoration was a later addition, as underneath are floral motifs and lettering in full, "For the Head" on one, and "For the Arm" on the other.

Gift of Louis M. Rabinowitz, Brooklyn, N. Y.

                                                    PLATE LXXXII

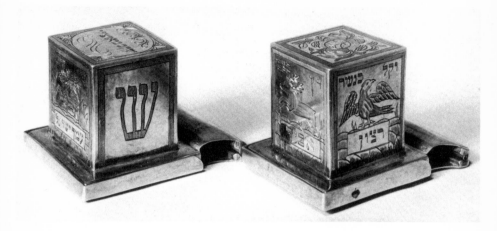

161

162

151   Plate LXXXII

MARRIAGE

The marriage ceremony, according to Jewish custom, is accompanied by a contract for which in previous centuries a beautifully decorated parchment (*K'tubah*) was used. While the wedding ring which the bridegroom gave to his bride to keep, as symbol of the legality of their marriage, was to be a simple circlet, it need not necessarily have been used in the wedding ceremony itself. The rings on display here were used in the ceremonies. In many cases they were not owned by individuals, but remained the property of the congregation. They were worn by the newly-wed women during the week following the marriage ceremony. Sometimes these rings are crowned by a small synagogue building.

°163. MARRIAGE RING   LSA 301
 Gold filigree and enamel.
 H. 1½″ D. 1¼″
 Italy, 17th century
 Circlet decorated with building. Hinged roof lifts and reveals inscribed names, "Leib" and "Yntla."
 Lent by Sholem Asch, London, England
             PLATE LXXXIII

°164. MARRIAGE RING   LSA 302
 Gold, with silver floral decoration.
 H. 1½″ W. ¾″
 Italy, 16th century
 Small synagogue. Inscription on roof, "To kindle the Sabbath Lights."
 Note arched openings similar to ring No. 14, *Jewish Encyclopedia*, 1907, vol. 10, p. 429.
 Lent by Sholem Asch, London, England
             PLATE LXXXIII

°165. MARRIAGE RING   LSA 303
 Gold, with filigree and enamel decoration.
 H. ¾″ W. ⅞″
 Italy, 17th century
 Similar to ring No. 11; *Jewish Encyclopedia*, 1907, vol. 10, p. 429.
 Lent by Sholem Asch, London, England
             PLATE LXXXIII

°166. MARRIAGE RING   F 450
 Gold, with filigree decorations.
 Italy, 18th century
 Inscription: "Good luck."
 Harry G. Friedman Collection
             PLATE LXXXIII

°167. MARRIAGE RING   L 13-54
 Gold.
 H. 2″ D. 1″
 Italy, 18th century
 Lent by the Museum of the Hebrew Union College, Cincinnati, O.
             PLATE LXXXIII

°168. MARRIAGE RING   17.190.996
 Gold and enamel.
 Venice, Italy, 16th century
 Inscription: "MT" for Mazal Tob (Good Luck).
 Metropolitan Museum of Art, N. Y. C.
             PLATE LXXXIII

163

164

165

166

167

168

153

PLATE LXXXIII

169

Parchment, illuminated.
H. 17″   W. 14″
Amsterdam, Holland, 1693 (date of printing)

Colored bird and floral motifs in side panels. Left, figure of Charity; right, man and woman holding hands; center, text of marriage contract, 1718.

Gift of Harry G. Friedman to Library of The Jewish Theological Seminary of America.

PLATE LXXXIV

PLATE LXXXIV   154

170a

170b

170c

*170a, b, c. COFFEE SERVICE—CREAMER,
SUGAR BOWL AND TRAY

L 2-49 a, b, c

Old English salt-glaze Staffordshire china.

A wedding gift. Decorated with fish scale design in red and
other motifs in apple-green. Tray decorated with a scene of a
wedding ceremony, showing the bridal couple, the rabbi and
the two witnesses.

Inscriptions: On tray, "Let God rejoice over you as a bridegroom rejoices over his bride." On sugar bowl, "Amsterdam,
1769, on the 24th day of the month of Sivan (June)." Other
inscriptions state that the set was given to Hillel, son of Tevia,
and his bride, Brendelah, by Zvi Hirsh, son of Abraham.

Lent by Mrs. Felix M. Warburg

PLATE LXXXV

155

PLATE LXXXV

MEZUZAH

The *Mezuzah* is a parchment scroll in a tube of metal or wood, placed on the upper part of the right doorpost of a house or an occupied room slanting toward the left. The parchment contains two portions of the Pentateuch (Deut. 6.4-9 and 11.13-21), the Jewish profession of faith, and passages dealing with God's love and His commandments. The tube or case usually has a small opening through which may be seen the Hebrew word for "Almighty," written on the back of the parchment. The name *Mezuzah*, the Hebrew word for doorpost, refers to the sentence "Thou shalt write them upon the doorpost of thy house, and upon thy gates" (Deut. 6.9 and 11.20).

°171. MEZUZAH   F 3189

> *Wooden holder containing parchment manuscript.*
> *L. 10½″   W. 2¼″*
> *Galicia, ca. 1850*

Rectangular wooden holder with the word "Shaddai" (Almighty) in circular opening. Carved ornaments: crown above two peacocks.

Harry G. Friedman Collection

PLATE LXXXVI

°172. MEZUZAH   F 665

> *Silver case containing text from the Pentateuch, written on*
> *parchment.*
> *L. 8″   W. 2¾″*
> *Breslau, 1804-1813*
> *Hallmark: Hintze 23, with year letter N*
> *Master: Carl Gottlieb Freytag (Hintze 181)*

Two small doors open to reveal the word "Shaddai" (Almighty) written on a parchment scroll and containing text from Deut. 6.4, 9 and 11.13, 21.

Harry G. Friedman Collection

PLATE LXXXVI

°173. MEZUZAH   F 3180

> *Parchment manuscript in wooden container.*
> *L. 10″   W. 1¾″*
> *Jerusalem, 19th century*

In relief, Rachel's Tomb, and the Wailing Wall in Jerusalem.
Harry G. Friedman Collection

PLATE LXXXVI

171

172

173

157

Plate LXXXVI

BURIAL SOCIETY — *HEBRAH KADDISHA*

The *Hebrah Kaddisha,* meaning "Holy Society," was the organization for the burial of the dead. Membership in it was an esteemed privilege. The *Hebrah Kaddisha* frequently had its own meeting house. On a certain day, usually the 7th of *Adar,* the traditional day of Moses' death, members observed a fast, at the end of which a festive meal was served. Large wine cups were used on such occasions. Frequently such cups were engraved with the names of departed members and were accordingly treasured. It was customary for members to wear special attire of Spanish origin, consisting of a black mantle with flat cap. (An outstanding cup showing such costumes is the glass from Polin, F 3211, Cat. No. 174, Pl. LXXXVII, Jewish Museum, N. Y. C.)

°174-174a. CUP FOR BURIAL SOCIETY
(HEBRAH KADDISHA)   F 3211

Glass, enamelled.
H. 9¾″   D. 5¼″
Bohemia or Hungary, 1692

Members of the Hebrah Kaddisha in medieval dress, in procession preceding and following casket. Inscription: "This glass belongs to the Holy Burial Society of the Congregation of Polin. A gift from Moses, son of Jacob Polin, Hanukkah 1692." (Inscription is upside down.)

A similar glass (once in the synagogue treasure of Unterberg-Eisenstadt, Hungary) is now in the Bezalel Museum, Jerusalem; also, another glass of this type was in an Austrian Collection.

Harry G. Friedman Collection

PLATE LXXXVII

°175. CUP FOR BURIAL SOCIETY
(HEBRAH KADDISHA OF WORMS)   JM 30-51

Silver, with engraved inscription.
H. 9¾″   D. (lip) 4⅛″
Nuremberg, Germany, 1712 (R³ 3762)
Master: ICW (Johann Conrad Weiss) (R³ 4279)

Hexagonal cup tapering downwards to a broader hexagonal base. Walls are covered with names of members of burial society. Companion piece dated 1732 (JM 31-51, Jewish Museum, N. Y. C.) continues the list of members.

Top inscription indicates cup was for the holy burial society. Date, 1712, indicated by dotting letters in inscription from Ps. 33.19, "To deliver their soul from death and to maintain them in prosperity." The word "prosperity" in this inscription is substituted for the word "famine" in the Psalm.

See J. Kiefer, "Zum 900-jaehrigen Bestehen der Synagoge zu Worms," *Zeitschrift fuer die Geschichte der Juden in Deutschland,* vol. 5, 1934, p. 104.

Gift of Michael Oppenheim, Mainz, Germany
PLATE LXXXVIII

174

174a

PLATE LXXXVII

175

Plate LXXXVIII   160

MISCELLANEOUS OBJECTS

*176. CUTOUT PARCHMENT   JM 51-51

H. 14″   W. 12⅛″
Galicia, 1846

Cutout and interlaced designs. Chief motifs: Open Torah Ark;
above it stylized rendering of Seven-Branched Candlestick, and
many other motifs similar to those on Torah curtains, arranged
in form of a Mizrah (meaning "East," to designate the direction
of prayer). While this item does not show the word Mizrah,
it may nonetheless have been used as one.

The text consists of lengthy quotations from the Bible, portions
from the Book of Deuteronomy and the Psalms. It is supposed
to have been made by a student of a Polish institution of higher
learning, upon the occasion of his graduation.

Gift of Mr. and Mrs. George Sagan, N. Y. C.

PLATE LXXXIX

176

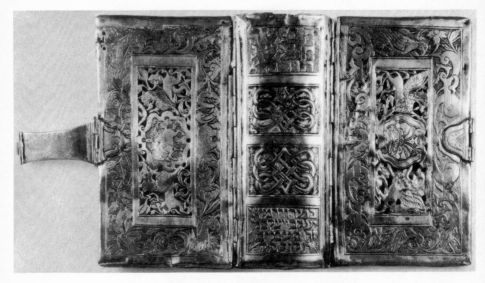

177

°177. PRAYER BOOK COVER   F 3516

Silver, partly gilded, engraved and openwork.
5½″ x 3¼″   D. 2½″
Poland, 1740

Front cover: Broad border, flowers and animals; in center, rectangular panel, unicorn on cartouche between lions. Back cover border: Scroll work and birds; outer crown in cartouche between griffons.

Back with interlaced ornaments and inscription; above "Five Books of the Torah," inscription below the name Maier Jacob and quotation: "For he hath supplanted me then two times," (Gen. 27.36).

Harry G. Friedman Collection

PLATE XC

PLATE XC   162

178

°178. PRAYER BOOK   F 2552

Silver filigree.
H. 4¼″   W. 3″
Amsterdam, Holland, 1760

Cartouche on front cover engraved with rampant lion facing a crowned tree. Cartouche on back cover engraved with pitcher and basin for an owner who was a Levite. Small piece of filigree work of binding rod is missing. The filigree is of the Italian type, similar to Amulets Nos. F 2149 and F 2150, Jewish Museum, N. Y. C.

PLATE XCI

179

°179. PRAYER BOOK BINDING   F 3684

*Silver gilt with metal embroidery on green velvet set with pearls
and garnets.*
H. 8¾″   W. 6″
Italy, mid-19th century

Openwork floral designs on green velvet. Front cover: Medallion
surrounded by leaf-motifs, containing cartouche in center with
enamelled roundel, showing the hands of the priest as he blesses
the congregation; above the hands the Crown of Priesthood,
below clouds.

Back cover: Central cartouche with coat of arms, showing a
tower surmounted by lion, other lion to the right.

Back of binding in open metal work; a central cartouche with
initials SKM.

Prayerbook is in Hebrew with Italian translation (Vienna, 1846)
according to Ashkenazic rite, translation by Rabbi Lelia della
Torre.

Harry G. Friedman Collection

PLATE XCII

180. WINE GLASS   L 17-54

Tumbler with gold and red decorations.
H. 4½″   D. 2¾″
Austria, inscription date 1796
Decorated at the Weinsperger Forest
Maker: Milner

Cut and fitted with two rings and curved plate on the side

PLATE XCII   164

(lower ring missing). Upper ring in red and gold, with an inner inscription. The plate covers a portrait in color and a red and gold border with inscription, all on a silver backing.
Inscription: Around portrait: "In honor of a good friend." Lower part: "Made by Milner at Gutenbrunn, on the edge of the Weinsperger Forest, 1796." Also poems in praise of a man named David, to whom presumably the glass was presented.
Lent by Jerome Strauss Collection, N. Y. C.

181. BOWL   F 3450

Bronze, engraved.
H. 3½″ D. 9″
Persia, 18th century

Inside, center: Pigeon with spread wings, surrounded by sunbursts. Also cabalistic inscriptions referring to the constellations, the rivers in Paradise, etc. Owner: "Zebi Hayim Moses, son of Phineas." Inscription, outside: "And the Lord shall take away from thee all sickness . . ." (Deut. 7.15).
Harry G. Friedman Collection

°182-182a. PEN CASE (WITH INKWELL) FOR SCRIBE   F 3445

Silver, partly gilded, embossed and engraved.
L. 8½″ W. 2″ H. 1½″
Persia, 1676
Arabic Mastermark on bottom

Floral decorations and elaborate inscriptions on case and on inner tray. Scene of trial and punishment (on bottom of case) unrelated to the pious inscriptions.
According to inscriptions, this case was given in 1676 by Elihu to his son Joseph. The donor enumerates his forbears as follows: David, Rahamin, Isaac, Zebulon, Moses, Elihu. Other inscriptions include quotations from Ps. 90.17 and 32.7; Gen. 49.22 (the allusion is to his son Joseph); and the cabalistic prayer, "Lo, with the power of Thy mighty right hand . . ."; concluding with a prayer for divine assistance throughout life.
Harry G. Friedman Collection

PLATE XCIII

183. LAVER (TWO HANDLES, WITH LID)   F 82

Silver with engraved and cast decorations.
H. (with lid) 6¾″ D. 4¾″
Eastern Europe
Mastermark: ILO
Weight mark: 12 with star

Used for ceremonial washing of the hands by Kohanim (those of priestly origin), before the ceremony of blessing the congregation on holidays. Decorations around body of laver: twelve signs of the Zodiac with their corresponding Hebrew names for the months.
Harry G. Friedman Collection

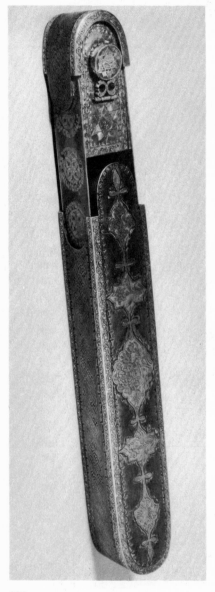

182

182a

PLATE XCIII   166

184

*184. LAVER FOR WASHING OF HANDS   S 80

Silver, repoussé and embossed work.
D. 23½″
Turin, Italy, ca. 1790 (R³ 7470 with D 11)
Mastermarks: CV (R 7480) and PL

Used for ceremonial washing of hands by Kohanim (those of priest by descent), before the ceremony of blessing the congregation on holidays. Pitcher missing. Decorations in the style of Louis XVI: Center, pitcher and laver. On rim, between acanthus scrolls, Abraham, Isaac, Jacob, Moses, Aaron, David and Solomon.

Laver from the same workshop was in the Esposizione Ebraica, Milan, Italy, 1934, catalogue pp. 12-13.

PLATE XCIV

185

Brass, hammered and embossed decorations.
H. 34″ W. 24″
Eastern Europe, 18th century

Sides, the two columns of the Temple. Top, crown between
two birds. Below this, ribbon cartouche held by rampant lions.
Inscriptions: "Know before whom thou standest . . ." (Talmud,
Berakhoth 28 b). "I have set the Lord always before me"
(Ps. 16.8).

According to this verse, which in the Hebrew text begins with
the word, "Shivithi," a plate like this was called a Shiviti. It
stood on the desk in front of the cantor who faced the Ark.

Its practical use was that of a sounding board for the cantor's
voice.

PLATE XCV